D1478742

MEMORIES
FROM PARIS
TO STANFORD

*Les souvenirs sont des fleurs fraiches que
l'on fait avec des fleurs fanées*

*Memories are fresh flowers
made from wilted ones**

*[Poetic phrase written in French by Ernest Léwy]

The author at age 5 on his balcony in Paris

MEMORIES FROM PARIS TO STANFORD
Life, Particles and Politics

Gregory A. Loew

REGENT PRESS
Berkeley, California
2023

[HARDBACK]
ISBN 10: 1-58790-646-5
ISBN 13: 978-1-58790-646-6

[E-BOOK]
ISBN 10: 1-58790-647-3
ISBN 13: 978-1-58790-647-3

Library of Congress Catalog Number: 2023017889

MANUFACTURED IN THE U.S.A.
REGENT PRESS
Berkeley, California
www.regentpress.net

Contents

Foreword

This book is a memoir of my long and lucky life.

I am lucky to have had caring parents who saved our family from the horrors of WW2 and gave my siblings and me a good education. I was lucky as an adolescent to know early on what I wanted to do when I grew up: I wanted to pursue a career in physics rather than join my father's business which he thought might be more lucrative.

When WW2 came to an end with the atomic bombing of Hiroshima and Nagasaki, the terror of nuclear war didn't immediately dawn on me. However, my sudden awareness of Einstein's mysterious $E_0=mc^2$ formula increased my curiosity about physics even further.

I am lucky that I ended up at Stanford University where I had a wonderful education and career.

Finally, I am lucky that at my age my memory is still essentially intact.

Introduction

This memoir comes in three consecutive parts:

PART 1, which includes Chapters 1 and 2, presents the highlights of my personal life, my education, and my marriage.

PART 2, which includes chapters 3 to 18, is a description of my fifty-year professional career at SLAC National Accelerator Laboratory where I participated in some fascinating accelerator and particle physics research. Many people are convinced *a priori* that this type of science is beyond their comprehension, but my ambition here is to make it as understandable as possible to my readers, regardless of their backgrounds. My career took me all over the world and brought me together with wonderful colleagues at home and abroad, whose contributions and memories I want to share.

PART 3, which includes Chapters 19 to 23, covers some of my observations and experiences in world affairs and politics that enriched my life. My decision to teach courses on *the causes of war* at Stanford also explains how I came to publish a book in 2019 on *The Human Condition,* and why this memoir frequently includes comments on international events. After I retired, I also found some time to study the existential threat of global warming of our planet to which I dedicate Chapter 22.

Additional interviews, Power Point presentations and documents can be found on my website **GregoryLoew.com**

Acknowledgments

In addition to my parents, relatives, colleagues and friends mentioned in this book, I wish to acknowledge the special advice and help I received from my brother Sebastian Loew, my son George Loew, my daughters Linda Maki and Florence Surratt, and my good friend Ben Lenail. Their encouragement and contributions were very much appreciated. I also want to thank my former colleague at SLAC, Terry Anderson, for designing the cover of this book, and SLAC's Gregory Stewart for many of his illustrations.

PART 1

Chapter 1

Highlights of my early personal life (1930-1954)

My family genealogy is complicated. My paternal grandfather, Theodore Loew, was born in Prague and my grandmother, Anna Kornfeld, in Vienna. My father, Georges Loew, was born in Bucharest, Romania where some of his family had moved for business reasons. Because of his father's origins, in 1914 my father was drafted into the Austro-Hungarian cavalry and sent with an occupation force to Kiev, Ukraine, as part of the war against Czarist Russia. He lived in Kiev for about three years with a Jewish family, and as far as I know, was not involved in combat. On the other hand, I recall him telling me about his liaison with his landlords' daughter. Fate, however, had it that in 1917, he had to leave. A series of chaotic revolutionary upheavals broke out in Ukraine, and as a result he was sent to the Italian front where he was wounded. After WW1 ended in 1918, he returned to Bucharest. Meanwhile, unlike Putin's currently attempted but so far thwarted invasion, the Bolsheviks succeeded in incorporating Ukraine into the USSR in 1922.

My maternal grandfather, Alfred Cohen, was born in Hamburg, Germany, and grandmother, Carolina Hahn, in Guasipati, Venezuela, of German parents. As an aside, she was the cousin of Reynaldo Hahn, the Venezuelan/French composer and future lover of Marcel Proust. My mother, Elisabet Cohen, was born and raised in Hamburg. My parents met at their best friends' wedding there in 1928, and married in Hamburg in 1929, right after the beginning of the Great Depression. They then moved to Bucharest for two years, immediately after their wedding.

Following, you can see my parents, Georges and Elisabet Loew on their wedding day, standing behind my mother's parents Carolina and Alfred Cohen in their Hamburg garden (Fig. 1).

1

To please all my grandparents, I was brought into this world in 1930 in Vienna in an excellent modern clinic. Even though my parents were secular Jews, by Austrian law my birth certificate was issued by the local Jewish Community Center. A few weeks later, they returned with me to Bucharest (of which I remember nothing) until 1932. My parents then fulfilled their dream to settle in Paris where my father moved his business. This explains why from then on, we always spoke French in my family even though they originally spoke German with each other and me.

As I look back to my childhood and adolescence, I must thank my parents who offered unique opportunities and experiences to me and my siblings Monique Loew (born in Paris in 1934 and deceased there in 2020) and Sebastian Loew, born in Paris in 1939 and currently an urban designer, living in London. Our father was not only a successful businessman but also an excellent pianist (with perfect ear) who exposed us to classical music and operas from an early age. He was also very interested in politics and a passionate mountain climber as I will describe later. Our mother was a wonderful teacher with the patience of Job and she was very artistic with water coloring, tapestry, bookbinding, and photography. She also had a hobby of taking note of incidents and encounters that happened *par hasard* (by coincidence) of which you will find plenty in this book. Incidentally, my mother was a cousin of Margaret and H.A. Rey, the authors of *Curious George*.

Paris (1933-1939)

Paris was fabulous but, sadly, our life there wasn't going to last very long. Hitler had come to power in Germany, fascism and antisemitism were rampant all over Europe, and communism had taken hold in the USSR.

Had I understood some of this, I would not have been shocked when a little playmate of mine in the Bois de Boulogne told me that he was no longer allowed to play with me because his parents had found out that I was Jewish.

At age 6, I began school at the Cours Hattemer in Paris. This was a very special school that one attended for only one morning per week with at least one parent sitting in the back of the class. The teacher gave a short exam and assigned all the material to be learned during the subsequent week. All the home teaching was done by my patient mother at home. When we traveled, the homework was mailed to us wherever we were.

Our parents loved traveling and skiing in St Moritz, Switzerland where we stayed at the wonderful Suvretta House Hotel. When I was about 5 years old, we had actress Hedy Lamar sitting at the table next to ours in the dining room and I am told she flirted with me because I looked "cute". Not bad, although I don't remember our relationship.

Up till 1938, we could still safely visit my grandparents in Hamburg during the winter holidays. My grandfather, however, was very naïve and thought that the Nazis couldn't touch them. When they finally left Germany on April 5th, 1939 for London, they were forced to sell their house for a pittance and allowed to leave with 5 Marks each in their pockets. They then lived through the whole Blitz in London.

Seen top of next page with me is my first sibling, my sister Monique who was born in Paris in 1934 (Fig. 2). As sweet and loving as we both looked in this picture, we soon also learned about fighting and sibling rivalry. Check out famous psychoanalyst Alfred Adler on this subject for more details.

Babar was the first book I read and loved (Fig. 3). Little did I know that I would meet BaBar again sixty years later as the B quark-antiquark pair at SLAC.

At this age, I also began my first stamp collection, and I

2

3

learned many interesting facts from it. Kenya-Uganda-Tanganyika had beautiful triangular stamps. The most expensive stamp in the world was from the Mauritius Island. And the French Post Office had to retract the stamp celebrating the 200th anniversary of Descartes' *Discours de la Méthode* because it had misprinted it as *Discours sur la Méthode*: a gaffe that made the few people who bought the first edition instantaneously rich. I also enjoyed going to the Marché aux Timbres at the Rond Point des Champs-Elysées. It was right next to the children's Guignol, the famous Paris puppet theater (guignol) which I also frequented.

Politically, France in those years was still living under the parliamentary system of the Third Republic. Albert Lebrun was a respected President, but he had very little power. There was considerable socio-economic tension in the country and Socialist Léon Blum became Prime Minister leading the *Front Populaire* in 1936, with support of the Communist Party.

In 1937 Paris hosted the unforgettable International Expo 37 along the Seine. Note in this prophetic picture the Soviet (right) and German (left) pavilions facing each other (Fig. 4). The newly built Palais de Chaillot is in back.

In March 1938, Hitler annexed Austria. This move was called the *Anschluss*. From then on, it became evident that he would not hesitate to start a war to get his way. In France we had to acquire gas masks to be prepared for the worst.

Later in 1938 came the disastrous meeting in Munich in September when Chamberlain and Daladier appeased Hitler and Mussolini, all seen right (Fig. 5), over the annexation of the Sudetenland.

Note, however, that at the time people were so afraid of another world war that the Munich "accord" was widely received with a sigh of relief: "Peace in our time," said Chamberlain.

In February 1939, Hitler occupied Bohemia and Moravia and dismembered the rest of Czechoslovakia by making Slovakia a satellite state. The Allies failed to mount any resistance.

By that time, we had moved into a modern new apartment on the rue de la Pompe, in preparation for the birth of our little

4

5

brother Sebastian. He arrived on June 6th to the great excitement of the entire family. There was also room in the apartment for a newly acquired Steinway grand piano which, much to my father's delight, permitted me to start piano lessons at home. I remember painfully struggling with scales and Diabelli exercises.

In Spring 1939, I also remember witnessing the fabulous parade in celebration of the visit of King George VI in Paris with President Lebrun. They now had a strong alliance, *l'Entente Cordiale.* The parade was escorted by the magnificent camel mounted Moroccan Spahis. I was so impressed that I can still visualize them today! [Sixty years later during a scientific meeting at CERN, I met an engineer by the name of Lebrun. When I discovered that he was the President's grandson, I told him about this parade, and he was impressed as well.]

In August, our family went on vacation to beautiful Evian on the French side of Lake Geneva, from where the well-known mineral water comes. The vacation was pleasant, but the international situation was becoming more ominous every day. Pretty soon we had eerie blackouts on the French side every night, with the Swiss side glowing with bright lights. On August 23rd, Germany and Russia signed the Molotov-Ribbentrop non-aggression pact which gave Hitler and Stalin secret permission to both invade and divide Poland.

In this troubling atmosphere, we returned to Paris on August 31st. The next morning, claiming to have been attacked during the night by Polish soldiers (Germans in disguise), Hitler indeed invaded Poland. The Allies then declared war on Germany on September 3rd, and WW2 began.

For fear of bombardments by the Luftwaffe, all families with children were ordered by the government to evacuate Paris immediately. We left for Brittany and eventually ended up for three months in a two-room apartment with our mother and a nanny (the Nounou who later came with us to Argentina).

If it hadn't been for my father's political savvy and courageous decision to leave France in December 1939 and move to
Argentina, I probably wouldn't be around to tell this story.

The trip by boat was not without risk because of the scary
submarine warfare in the Atlantic. We finally sailed on an Italian steamer out of Genoa because Italy had not yet entered the
war. The journey was very eventful. The French secret service
had discovered that there was a female member of the German
fifth column on board, and during the first night, a French
cruiser stopped our boat in the Mediterranean and took us
into custody to Marseille. There everybody had to disembark
until the woman was arrested. We were then let go. Our next
stop was Barcelona where we witnessed the terrible destruction
left by the Spanish Civil War. From there it was smooth sail-
ing to the Canary Islands, to Brazil with stops in Recife, Bahia
and Rio. However, we finally arrived in the estuary of the Rio
de la Plata shortly after the German Graf Spee battleship was
blocked there by several powerful British warships. Unable to
escape, the German captain scuttled his ship off the coast of
Montevideo (Fig. 6). Fortunately, our Italian S/S Oceania did

6

not get involved in this dramatic battle, which Churchill describes in his memoirs. We arrived safely in Buenos Aires on January 1st, 1940 and had the pleasure of being met by our very dear Uncle Rodolfo who already lived there.

Argentina (1940-1948)

In Argentina, we had to start a completely new life, become familiar with a new culture, and learn Spanish which we did in no time.

Starting in May 1940, the Germans and Italians began to overrun most of Europe, and our hearts sank. Maréchal Pétain caved in. Any contact with the old continent became impossible. The only world leaders that boosted our morale at the time were Winston Churchill (Fig. 7) when he became Prime Minister on May 10th, 1940, and Général Charles de Gaulle (Fig. 8) when he gave his famous speech in London on June 18th, 1940 (Fig. 9).

7

8

A TOUS LES FRANÇAIS

La France a perdu une bataille!
Mais la France n'a pas perdu la guerre!

Des gouvernants de rencontre ont pu capituler, cédant à la panique, oubliant l'honneur, livrant le pays à la servitude. Cependant, rien n'est perdu!

Rien n'est perdu, parce que cette guerre est une guerre mondiale. Dans l'univers libre, des forces immenses n'ont pas encore donné. Un jour, ces forces écraseront l'ennemi. Il faut que la France, ce jour-la, soit présente à la victoire. Alors, elle retrouvera sa liberté et sa grandeur. Tel est mon but, mon seul but!

Voila pourquoi je convie tous les Francais, où qu'ils se trouvent, à s'unir à moi dans l'action, dans le sacrifice et dans l'espérance.

Notre patrie est en peril de mort.
Luttons tous pour la sauver!

VIVE LA FRANCE !

GÉNÉRAL DE GAULLE

QUARTIER-GÉNÉRAL,
4, CARLTON GARDENS,
LONDON, S.W.1

9

For the record: it wouldn't be until June 22nd, 1941 that Hitler drew Russia into WW2, and until December 7th that Franklin D. Roosevelt declared war on the Axis.

When the Germans invaded Paris, our father was completely cut off from his tank car business which the Nazis confiscated, together with all our other belongings, identified as Jewish property. By necessity he had to change fields and he started an import-export business with the U.S.

We were lucky that in 1940 Argentina was an incredibly prosperous immigrant country. It had the fourth largest GDP in the world thanks to its immense agricultural resources. Unfortunately, its wealth was concentrated in the hands of a rich upper class while half the population lived in poverty. For much of its history, Argentina had its elected governments overthrown by authoritarian military coups. This is what happened once again in 1943 when a very conservative civilian government was overthrown by the military. Under this pro-Axis government, Coronel Juan Domingo Peron gained rapid prominence by pandering to the underprivileged classes. Argentina finally declared war on Germany just before it surrendered in May 1945, but by now General Peron, a demagogue with understandable mass appeal with his wife Evita Duarte (both seen below, Fig. 10), got himself legally elected President in early 1946.

10

Peron as President passed several generous pro-labor laws, but he was no Franklin Roosevelt. He squandered Argentina's wealth, caused an endless deficit and inflationary spiral, and created a huge bureaucracy. He also let himself be fooled by Austrian physicist Richter (no relation to SLAC's Burton Richter) into funding a fraudulent nuclear fusion project in Bariloche on the Isla Huemul. In the end he lost the support of the military and the Catholic Church, and he was overthrown by another military coup in 1955. Unfortunately, there is still much income and education inequality in the country seventy years later, his Peronista and Kirschnerista successors are still venerating his memory, and the Argentine economy is still in a constant state of inflation, financial domestic and foreign deficit.

This said, Argentina is a country with immense natural beauty, cultural life, talented artists and musicians, world-class scientists from the Instituto Balseiro in Bariloche, and last but not least Pope Francis! Buenos Aires has spectacular avenues, monuments, parks and plazas, the beautiful Teatro Colon opera house, outstanding soccer players, tango singers and dancers, and the country's steakhouses are the best in the world.

The famous Cabildo on the Plaza de May in Buenos Aires where Argentina's independence movement from Spain began on May 25th, 1810, is shown on the next page (Fig. 11).

In Buenos Aires, my siblings and I attended a good private French school called "*Le Collège Français de Buenos Aires.*" What was special about it was that during the first six grades, all the instruction at this school was in Spanish in the morning and in French in the afternoon. Starting in high school, it was only in French. Some of my teachers in math and science were excellent and I knew from an early age that I wanted to pursue a career in physics. I met my first girlfriend, Gaby Maier, there and made many lifelong friends like Serge and Michel Hurtig, and others. Of these, unfortunately only Lucien Matalon is still alive. We all graduated together by successfully passing our two French

11

"bachots" (baccalaureates) at the French Embassy in Buenos Aires in 1946 and 1947.

With his passion for mountains, our father soon discovered the beautiful Nahuel Huapi national park around San Carlos de Bariloche, in the Andes. He was the eighth to climb the majestic

12

Cerro Tronador straddling the border with Chile, seen lower left from the Cerro Lopez (Fig. 12).

A year later, my parents bought a piece of land in Bariloche and subsequently built a chalet where we spent many wonderful summers climbing mountains, as well as skiing in the winters.

13

Shown here are my father, me, Monique, my mother and Sebastian in front of our chalet in Bariloche, January 1945 (Fig. 13).

In 1944, WW2 took a decisive turn on June 6th D-Day shown next page (Fig 14), and the subsequent liberation of Paris on August 23-25 that we celebrated in Buenos Aires with immense relief and joy.

WW2 ended de facto with Japan's surrender on August 15rh, 1945 immediately after the atomic bombings of Hiroshima and Nagasaki shown next page (Fig. 15).

14

15

New York (1945-1946)

After the war's end, we took our first trip to the United States. It was an unforgettable experience. We traveled by passenger/freighter boat via Rio, Curacao, Havana to Hoboken. The Hudson River upon our arrival was covered with ice. We stayed in a small apartment on the 25th floor of the then Park Central Hotel on 7th Avenue. The U.S. with WW2 had finally emerged from the Great Depression. Harry Truman had succeeded FDR and he was doing a good job. In comparison with Latin America, the U.S. was a bastion of Democracy. The GI Bill (free college for veterans!) was in full swing. I fell in love with New York. The city with Fifth Avenue, Broadway, Times Square, Rockefeller Center and the Empire State Building was mesmerizing. We had many relatives in town, most of them having escaped from Europe. Those who had been drafted were coming home. My cousin Theodore who was originally supposed to be parachuted in Romania with his brother Jean, had eventually landed in France after D-Day.

At age 15, I was gaining some independence. For a one-dollar standing room ticket, I discovered my interest for operas like Tannhauser and Rosenkavalier at the Met, and our whole family saw Toscanini conduct a fabulous Symphony of the Air concert at RCA. I also saw Stravinsky and heard him conducting his Firebird and modern music at Carnegie Hall (Fig. 16).

16

Our baby-sitter, Mrs. Kennedy, introduced us to jello, peanut butter and jelly sandwiches, and she taught us to play Mah-Jong. She was a liberal Democrat and kept writing letters of approval (or occasional disapproval) to Eleanor Roosevelt.

With great delight we became acquainted with the Horn and Hardart Automat Restaurant shown below (Fig. 17) with the three of us on Fifth Avenue.

17

We also traveled by car to Philadelphia, Washington D.C., visited Mount Vernon, and explored the magnificent National Art Gallery.

And just for the record, I show next page a piece of American advertising of the time publicizing slow-aged beer (Fig. 18)!

make mine
RUPPERT

Tasting is Believing

There's only one way to find out what a whale of a difference SLOW AGEING makes in the flavor of beer—and that's to try a glass of Ruppert. Compare it with any other beer.

SLOW AGED FOR FINER FLAVOR

JACOB RUPPERT, Brewery, New York City—1946

18

After three months in the U.S., we returned to Buenos Aires in March 1946 via several hops with Pan American's shaky DC4s. We were stopped in Miami unintentionally for several days because they discovered we didn't have transit visas through Brazil. It gave us a chance to see southern Florid, but we were a bit shocked to discover that beautiful beaches like Palm Beach were private and you couldn't access them without paying. Private enterprise had gone a bit too far! We then got home after three more stopovers in Belem, Rio, and Porto Alegre. Quite a first flying experience for us kids!

Paris (1948-1952)

Important events took place in the world in 1948: the creation of the State of Israel and the first war with the Arabs, the Berlin Airlift to counter the Russian blockade, the desegregation of the U.S. armed forces, the enactment of the Marshall Plan, and the reelection of President Harry Truman.

Despite all the tensions in Europe due to the Berlin Blockade and the Cold War, I returned to Paris in late 1948 to start my university studies at the Sorbonne. The Sorbonne was not the most up-to-date institution to study science in Paris, but it was very democratic. Anybody who had passed the two French baccalaureates in the world could register and study there for a fee of about 25 dollars per year. Classes were held in huge auditoriums with 300 students per class. The personal contact with professors was nil and you could never ask them a question. After class, you were entirely on your own. Studying alone took a huge amount of self-discipline.

The Fourth Republic in whose unstable parliamentary system de Gaulle refused to participate, had created a strong social safety net for the population, but had a hard time governing. The Communist Party under Maurice Thorez controlled more than 25% of the votes in the National Assembly, and there were constant strikes, plus the costly colonial wars in Indochina and Algeria. Despite this, my stay in Paris after the war was totally fascinating. The city had a vibrant cultural and artistic life. Famous writers like Camus and Sartre, and painters like Matisse could be seen in cafés. First-class theaters like the Comédie Francaise, André Barsacq's Théatre de l'Atelier and the Théatre Marigny featured outstanding actors like Maurice Escande, Louis Jouvet, Jean-Louis Barrault (as Baptiste in Marcel Carné's movie *Les Enfants du Paradis*) and his wife Madeleine Renaud. Dixieland jazz was heard all over, with Louis "Satchmo" Armstrong and

Sydney Bechet performing for free for students. [By the way, *par hazard* I sat next to Jean-Louis Barrault and Madeleine Renaud on a plane between Bueno Aires and Montevideo many years later and got invited to their theater in Paris.]

I lived at the Argentine Pavilion of the large Cité Universitaire where I made many wonderful and diverse friends from all over the world. The first year, Serge Hurtig, my friend (met in Buenos Aires) and mentor studying at Sciences Po, also stayed there. Later on I became friends with Joe Ainsworth (U.S. painter), Carlos Viacava (composer from Argentina), Mammo Tadesse (political science student from Ethiopia), Filoteo Samaniego (political science student from Ecuador), Jacques Guichard (architect student at the Beaux-Arts), Christian Tierny from Arras and Antonio Rojas Miranda from La Paz (medical students), Mircea Fotino (physics student with me from Bucharest), and Dang Wu Nhue (also physics student with me, from Hanoi). I also had a friend from Cameroun in my Math class, but I don't remember his name.

During my first summer vacation in 1949, I was invited with my friend Michel Hurtig to spend a month at the house of our former French nanny, Alice Colleu (aka Nounou) in northern Brittany, not far from Lamballe.

Nounou had joined our family in September 1939 to help my mother, and she had come with us to Argentina. She was a wonderful woman, a devout Catholic who never missed her Sunday mass, a patriotic supporter of de Gaulle, and she had a calligraphic handwriting, never forgetting to write for our birthdays. Her house, shown next page with us at the windows, was one of four buildings in the tiny bucolic village of St Glen (Fig. 19).

I show the place not just because we spent such a wonderful time there, eating like pigs and biking around the beautiful countryside, but because of a terrible event that had taken place there during WW2. It turns out that a Canadian pilot had been

19

shot down and parachuted close by. He made his way to the village and Nounou's mother, another staunch French patriot, who was living there alone, hid him in her attic. Unfortunately, after some time, the other people in the village began to gossip, and the Gestapo found out. They captured the pilot and sent Nounou's mother to a German concentration camp (Bergen-Belsen) where she died around age 65. Nounou who was still with us in Buenos Aires, didn't find out until July 1945. She was of course devastated and immediately returned to France. A few years later, she became the nanny for the children of the founder of the French weekly magazine l'Express, Jean-Jacques Servan Schreiber. At their house, she met all kinds of famous people like Prime Minister Pierre Mendès France who courageously ended the war in Indochina, and Jacqueline Bouvier (future wife of JFK). Nounou lived to be 100!

In winter I skied at Val d'Isère and Méribel-les-Allues, and in other summers I traveled to Italy where I visited my cousins in Milan, to London, and to Germany in 1951 where I witnessed all the destruction left from WW2. as seen in Hamburg upper right (Fig. 20).

38 GREGORY A. LOEW

20

While in Germany that year, I also visited my cousin Henry (Hans) Waldstein (brother of Margaret Rey) in Bonn where he was the legal advisor to U.S. High Commissioner in the American Zone, John McCloy. What got him this job was that he had studied law in Germany but was banned from practicing it when Hitler came to power. He then immigrated to the U.S. and got a second law degree in the U.S.

Sadly, in June 1950 when my parents were visiting me in Paris, the Korean War broke world peace once again. I will come back to this interminable conflict later, in reference to the U.N. Security Council veto. That summer, we attended the magnificent Salzburg musical festival and did our first climbs in Zermatt.

In July 1952 my parents came again to Europe from Argentina, this time with Monique and Sebastian, and they were of course very pleased that I had earned my Licence-ès-Sciences (undergraduate degree) in Mathematics, Physics, Chemistry and Radioactivity from the Sorbonne. The last year, I had had Irène Joliot-Curie, the daughter of Marie Curie as professor. I also

21

attended a few classes taught by the famous Louis de Broglie, but never could understand what he was saying and meticulously writing on the blackboard. He never looked at the audience.

In August my father and I climbed the Matterhorn in Zermatt as seen on the previous page (Fig. 21). It was a memorable adventure but at times quite scary! My mother was relieved to see us come back alive.

Pasadena (1952-1954)

After graduating from the Sorbonne, I came to the U.S for graduate school at Caltech in Pasadena in September 1952. As I travelled across the country by train, I had my first dramatic experience with the upcoming presidential campaign between Adlai Stevenson (nicknamed the Egg Head for his intellect) and WW2 hero Dwight "Ike" Eisenhower. The latter's VP candidate, Richard Nixon, had gotten himself into trouble with a dubious $18K campaign donation for which he needed to atone before the whole country. He did this shortly after the press revealed the scandal with his skillful tear-jerking Checkers speech. This was the name of an additional little dog gifted to his daughters. The nationwide speech was broadcast in the train. It did the trick, and Ike and he won in November.

Caltech was a mecca of science and engineering. Classes were tough but unlike at the Sorbonne, contact with the faculty was very close and easy. I was not quite ready for Richard Feynman's Quantum Mechanics course, but I attended his lectures which were riveting. Other luminaries like Nobel Laureate Robert Millikan of the famous oil drop experiment and Aeronautics Professor Theodore von Karman could be seen walking around the campus. And I often had dinner at the Athenaeum with Fred Hoyle of the Bing Bang he didn't believe in, and James Watson who had not yet announced the DNA double helix. Both were tight-lipped about their research,

My most congenial professors were Business Economist Horace Gilbert, and Lester Field who taught me a good course on electron devices. My close friends at Caltech were Luiz Dirickson and Gunther Perdigao from Brazil, Michel Bloch and Raymonde Patin from Paris, Cinna and Larissa Lomnitz from Chile, and Sitaram Rao Valluri from India. Valluri was the first to do experimental research on fatigue in metals. This earned him international fame, and several years later, he became director of the Indian Aeronautics Institute in Bangalore where I visited him and his wife Shyamala (Fig. 22).

22

Chapter 2

Deciding to move to Stanford for my Ph.D. (1954-1958)

Caltech was certainly a fabulous institute, but life there also had its downsides. Aside from the constant eye-irritating L.A. smog, a problem was that unless you were married, you felt like you were living in a monastery. There were no female students at the time and unless you owned a car, dates on the outside were essentially impossible. I mentioned this frustration to my empathetic professor Lester Field, and he wisely advised me to apply to do my Ph.D. at Stanford. Just before I got my M.S. degree in Electrical Engineering from Caltech in June 1954, Stanford offered me a generous scholarship for the next academic year, and in September I moved North to the Bay Area.

It was a momentous decision, but I didn't regret it. I immediately enjoyed the blue sky and the co-ed and more relaxed atmosphere at Stanford, then called the Farm. While I was a graduate student, I made many friends, Moe Lerner, Richard Pantell, Guy Benveniste, Jean-Louis and Catherine Barsacq, Jean-Louis Germain, Jacques Duroux, David and Catherine Colburn who were friends with 16-year-old Joan Baez, seen next page at a party at their house (Fig. 23), and Hannah Caldwell with her young children Haydi, Jim, Julie, Anne and Tony who all lived in a beautiful house in Atherton.

23

I also frequently met Stanford President Wallace Sterling and Provost Frederick Terman who were both very accessible. Terman had already become the father of yet-to-be named Silicon Valley, with the inception of companies like Hewlett Packard, Varian Associates and Watkins & Johnson.

Par hasard, to quote my mother again, I once met and had lunch in the cafeteria with Hoover scholar Alexander Kerensky. He was the man who, after the Czar's abdication in March 1917, had risen to head the Russian social democratic government for three months until, against all odds, he was overthrown by the Bolshevik revolution of October 1917. At Hoover he was now pondering over what he could have done differently to spare Russia from Lenin and Stalin. Given the unpopular war with Germany that Kerensky continued to support, it wasn't obvious.

My thesis supervisor at the Electronics Research Laboratory turned out to be Professor Karl Spangenberg, famous for his book on vacuum tubes. Somewhat prophetically, my thesis subject centered around a microwave amplifier and oscillator whose components resembled those of a linear electron accelerator.

Meanwhile, during the fall of 1956, the world scene was

shaken by the Hungarian Revolution promptly squelched by the Russians, and the Suez Canal crisis that led to the invasion of Egypt by Israel, France and the U.K.

I received my Ph.D. in Electrical Engineering on May 18th, 1958. Professor Spangenberg is shown below with me at his home on the day of my graduation (Fig. 24).

24

In June 1958, upon the recommendation of Professor Marvin Chodorow who had taught me Classical Mechanics, I started my fascinating scientific career at SLAC National Accelerator Laboratory that was initially called Project M (for Monster). For fifty years I worked there and at Stanford in various research, academic and managerial capacities, and between 2001 and 2005 I ended up being Deputy Director of SLAC.

Gilda (1930-2001)

At a party she gave for my colleague Peter and Marilyn Sturrock's wedding in September 1963, I met Gilda Thaw Harris, a very attractive divorced woman with three children. We danced together and immediately hit it off. She is shown below in 1965 (Fig. 25).

25

We got married in our recently bought house on August 9th, 1969. Gilda was a remarkable person because of her intelligence, strong convictions, and determination. Professionally, she was a U.C. Berkeley Ph.D. quantum chemist, and she did seminal work on the structure of hemoglobin and computer drug design. During our marriage she successively became an adjunct professor at the Stanford Medical School under Professor Joshua Lederberg, an adjunct professor at large at Rockefeller University, and the founder and leader of the not-for-profit Molecular Research Institute in Palo Alto. We lived together for over 30 years, but she died prematurely in 2001. Proceeds from her corporation were used to fund a Fellowship in her name for female science graduate students at Stanford.

Since we both worked full-time, we hired a wonderful house-keeper, Bertha Perez, to help us. She had a daughter, Adriana, who grew up in our house with our kids. Forty-seven years later, Bertha is still helping me.

My immediate family now consists of my three stepchildren, Paul, Linda and Neil, our two children, Florence and George, shown below, and eleven grandchildren from their respective marriages.

26

From left to right you can see me, Gilda, Linda, Paul, Florence, George and Neil behind him, on Gilda's 49th birthday in Pajaro Dunes on October 22nd, 1979 (Fig. 26). Not by coincidence, Linda, Neil and George went to Stanford, Paul to UC Berkeley and Florence to UC Santa Cruz.

We took many memorable trips together in the U.S., South America and Europe including our favorite cities like New York, Paris, London, Venice, Athens and Jerusalem.

Before I end these two chapters about my personal life, I want to come back once again to my parents. Their marriage was not always perfect, and my father could sometimes get very angry with all of us for no god reason. But throughout their life together, they had a loving relationship with each other. And this provided me with a good model, and positive memories.

They are seen below on their twentieth wedding anniversary (Fig. 27).

27

My father who had never really been sick in his life, died suddenly in Buenos Aires in 1961 at age 68 of a heart attack. It was a huge shock. Together with my siblings, our cousin Pedro Grunstein in Buenos Aires and Monsieur Gross, our father's chargé d'affaires in Paris, we were able to keep his businesses going for ten years.

My mother who visited with all of us frequently in Europe and in the U.S., died in Buenos Aires in 1987 at 83 of old age.

PART 2

Chapter 3

The origin of linear electron accelerators at Stanford

In 1957, a year before I got my Ph.D., a group of Stanford professors, Leonard Schiff, Felix Bloch, Robert Hofstadter, Wolfgang "Pief" Panofsky and Richard Neal, had submitted a proposal, shown below (Fig 28), to the U.S. government to build a two-mile long electron linear accelerator.

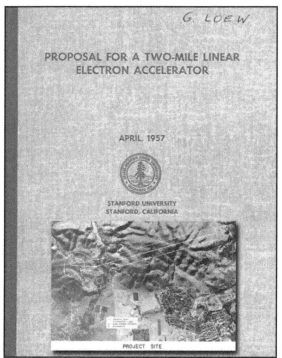

28

To understand the origin of this proposal, we must move back to the beginning of linear electron accelerators at Stanford with William W. Hansen shown below (Fig. 29).

29

When Hansen came to Stanford as a brilliant senior in 1928, atomic research was being done via X-ray scattering off material samples. Hansen soon realized when he joined the Physics Department in 1929 for research that this method was reaching its energy limits. As a result, he decided to look at electron scattering as the next approach. The way to give energy to electrons at the time was to connect the voltage of a DC power supply to produce an accelerating field across a vacuum tube with a hot cathode at one end, and an anode at the other. In the example shown top right (Fig. 30), the 200 kiloelectron volts (200 Kev) accelerated electrons could be extracted through a small hole in the anode to bombard the sample to be studied.

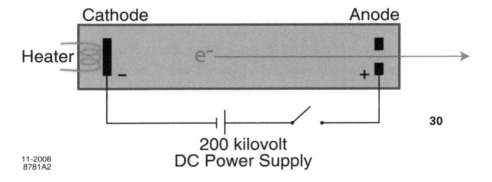

11-2008
8781A2

But this method was also limited in energy by the availability of high-voltage power supplies and their high cost. Several new ideas were needed. Hansen soon came up with the first idea shown below (Fig. 31).

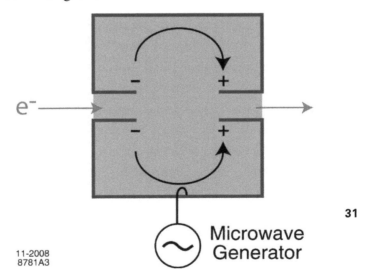

11-2008
8781A3

It consisted of a much less costly pulsed microwave generator connected to a re-entrant copper cavity where electrons entering from the left during half a cycle were accelerated toward the right. He built the first such prototype with a cavity he called the "rhumbatron" (after the back-and-forth rumba dance) driven by a 380 MHz (million cycles per second) triode oscillator. This device was a remarkable success, but the triode oscillator was too low in frequency and in power to produce a high enough accelerating voltage in the relatively large cavity.

The next big leap forward happened when the Varian brothers, Russell and Sigurd, joined Hansen at Stanford in 1936 with a very different motivation. Sigurd was an airplane pilot and he wanted to find a method to land at night or during a storm. For this he sought to generate a high-power microwave beam to bounce off and detect any obstacle in the dark. After some time, the three of them produced the first experimental device they called a klystron that could do such a job. Subsequently, in 1939, they built a sturdier klystron that was able to produce a microwave beam at 750 MHz (million cycles per second) in the atmosphere. This tube was transported to the Boston Airport where they used it to land a plane. It was probably the first practical experiment that would soon be called "radar!"

Soon thereafter, all three men moved to Long Island to do defense work for WW2 at the Sperry Gyroscope Corporation. At this company they also became acquainted with several other microwave specialists who would become involved in the linear accelerator business with them after the war.

Professor Fred Terman, famous for his book on Radio Engineering at Stanford, very much encouraged Bill Hansen to return to the university to resume his work on linear electron accelerators, which he did with enthusiasm. His next idea to make the accelerator more practical was to decrease the transverse size of the accelerating cavities and to link them together as shown above right (Fig. 32).

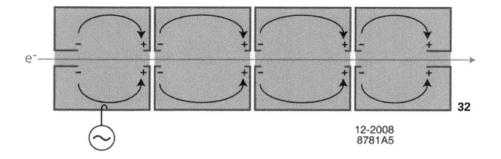

12-2008
8781A5

32

By supplying this array of contiguous cavities on the left where the electrons were also injected, he had created the traveling-wave linear accelerator. To make the acceleration of the electrons cumulative, he had to make the propagation velocity of the traveling wave synchronous with that of the electrons. Given that electrons are very light, they rapidly reach a velocity very close to the speed of light, making the design very simple and repetitive after a meter or so.

To proceed with the construction of the first operating linear accelerator. in 1946 Hansen enlisted the help of his colleague Ed Ginzton from Sperry and that of Richard B. Neal and several graduate students. By April 1947, the first linear accelerator at Stanford called Mark 1 shown next page (Fig. 33) with Bill Hansen, was completed. The driving microwave power frequency used was 2856 MHz (in the so-called S-band) and the energy gained by the electrons was 6 million electron volts (6 MeV).

Hansen was giving long monthly progress reports to his government sponsor, the Office of Naval Research, but on April 27th, the report just said:

"We have accelerated electrons."

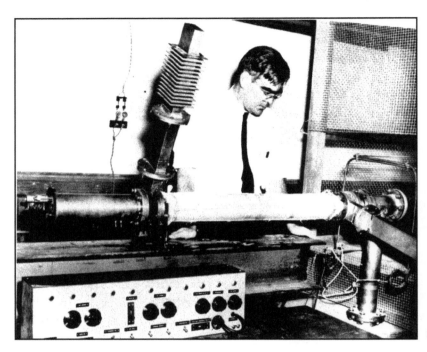

33

SLAC Electron Linac Principle

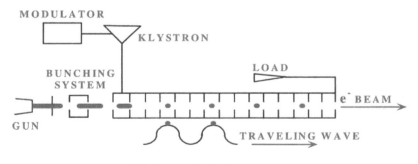

Disk-loaded Structure
$$\lambda_0 = 10.5 \text{ cm}$$
$$f = 2856 \text{ MHz}$$
$$E = \text{electron energy} \approx 10 \sqrt{P_{MW}} \text{ MeV}$$

34

What Hansen had built was the model of any injector to a traveling-wave linear electron accelerator such as for example the SLAC injector shown schematically lower left (Fig. 34). The energy in MeV of the emerging electrons on the right is shown to be proportional to the square-root of the klystron's peak power in megawatts for a ten-foot section running at 2856 MHz

In those days there was no Internet and scientists took longer to communicate with each other. Unbeknownst to Hansen, a group of scientists in the UK with similar ideas had beaten him to the task a few months earlier.

But in the long rivalry between Stanford and U.C. Berkeley, there was no doubt about Stanford's Hansen superiority: he could carry his accelerator on his shoulder with his three collaborators whereas at LBL, all the contributing scientists could do was to sit on theirs (Fig. 35)!

35

In fact, Hansen's ambitions were much greater. What he wanted to build was a 1 billion electron volt (1 GeV) multi-section linear accelerator to explore the scattering effect of electrons (shown in yellow) on protons and neutrons in the target (shown in green), in the schematic below (Fig. 36).

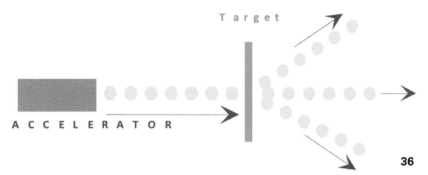

36

To do this, he first built a small model consisting of two accelerator sections in series, called the Mark II producing about 20 MeV electrons. When he got sufficient funds from the Office of Naval Research, he embarked on the much more complex new project that would be called the Mark III.

Tragically, in 1948 during the construction, Hansen became seriously ill and in March 1949, he died of lung disease, possibly due to poisoning from his earlier machining beryllium without proper protection. It was a huge loss for Stanford. Fortunately, the first phase of the Mark III was completed in 1952 under the management of Hansen's colleague Ed Ginzton, seen next page top (Fig. 37).

One of the people who helped Ginzton the most was graduate student Richard Neal who studied the theory of linear electron accelerators and all their sub-systems and components in detail and wrote his voluminous PhD thesis about this subject. This work greatly prepared him for his future SLAC career.

The Mark III accelerator at the Hansen High Energy Physics Laboratory (HEPL) was used by many particle physicists to do seminal experiments. Two of the most famous ones are shown lower right.

The first one was Robert Hofstadter (Fig. 38) who studied many atomic nuclei, work for which he received the Nobel Prize in Physics in 1961.

37

38

39

The second one was Wolfgang K.H. Pief Panofsky (Fig. 39) who did seminal work on pi mesons and became director of the Hansen High Energy Physics Laboratory.

The success of the entire Mark III enterprise between 1952 and 1957 was what led the Stanford scientists, by now already famous, to propose their daring and somewhat controversial project to the U.S. government.

When I was hired in 1958, funding for the project then called Project M (for Monster) was totally uncertain. The project staff consisted of only about 8 people led by overall Director Ed Ginzton. My boss was technical director Richard B. Neal who would become my wonderful mentor and supervisor for the next 24 years.

Chapter 4

My three years with Project M

For the first three years I was put in charge of designing the copper traveling microwave structures in which the electrons (or positrons) would be accelerated. With the help of colleague Bill Gallagher and my very able assistant Otto Altenmueller, I investigated many different structures and concluded that the original disk-loaded structure used by Hansen was still the most efficient. Arnold Eldredge, who oversaw mechanical fabrication, studied the possibility of electroforming the sections around an aluminum mandrel but eventually chose to use brazing of individual cavities by stacking them inside a vertical hydrogen furnace.

Each section would be ten feet long, consisting of 86 different cavities 1/3 of a 10.5 cm wavelength long. They were brazed together as shown next page top (Fig. 40) and sized to support a constant-gradient electric field. The full accelerator would consist of 960 such ten-foot traveling-wave sections (Fig. 41).

These prototype sections were tested in the two-klystron Mark IV linear accelerator that had been installed in the interim in the Hansen Microwave Laboratory where I had my office. This machine was also being used for experimental electron radiotherapy supervised by the Stanford Medical School.

During a vacation in Paris, I visited the Laboratoire de l'Accélérateur Linéaire (LAL) in Orsay for the first time and met

40

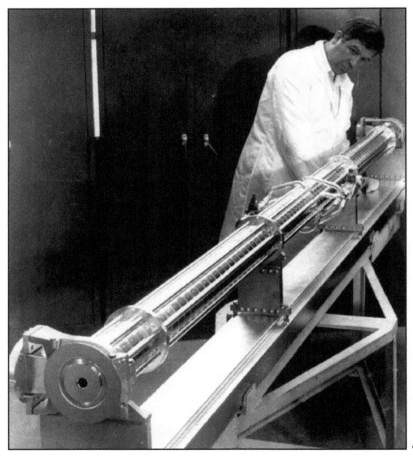

41

their very impressive director, Henri Leboutet. SLAC and LAL would have a long relationship in the years to come.

In 1959, then President Eisenhower announced that he would approve the construction of the accelerator for a total budget of $100 million, but the U.S. Congress was not yet convinced. After several more hurdles, our project was finally approved by Congress for $114 million on September 15th, 1961 under President John F. Kennedy. Our first funding agency was the Atomic Energy Commission, followed by the Energy Research and Development Administration (1975-1977) followed then by the Department of Energy thereafter.

September 1961 was also the time when I attended my first International Particle Accelerator Conference. It was principally devoted to the new circular proton accelerators, the Alternating (magnetic) Gradient Synchrotron (AGS) at Brookhaven National Lab and the Proton Synchrotron at CERN in Geneva. Ernest Courant (BNL) and John Adams (CERN) dominated the audience. I also got to know BNL's John Blewett (specialist of proton linear accelerators) and his wife Hildred (magnet design specialist) for whom I volunteered as a conference gopher.

To keep track of international events at this time, it should be mentioned that shortly after, JFK ordered the Bay of Pigs invasion in Cuba. A year later, 1962, the terrifying Cuban Missile Crisis shook the world.

The Stanford Board of Trustees was elated by our project's approval, and after some deliberations, on December 21st, the name of our laboratory was chosen to be the Stanford Linear Accelerator Center or SLAC for short.

Coincident with these wonderful developments, the two Varian brothers who had founded Varian Associates in 1948 to commercialize their klystron business with Bill Hansen and Ed Ginzton, unfortunately died. At this point, Ed Ginzton, the only survivor, decided he had to run the company full-time, and not being a particle physicist, he resigned from SLAC.

Pief Panofsky, the obvious candidate for the job, immediately became our fabulous director. He hired Matt Sands from Caltech as his deputy. Sands was succeeded a few years later by Stanford's Sidney Drell. Panofsky was not only an outstanding physicist, but he was also a wonderful human being. He had worked on the Manhattan Project, witnessed the Trinity Test of the first atomic bomb, and seen the effects of the Loyalty Oath imposed at UCRL that eventually caused him to resign from that lab and come to Stanford. When SLAC was funded, he had the wisdom to make it an internationally open institution with academic freedom and no classified work. Nobody would need a security clearance to work at SLAC. For the rest of his life, Panofsky worked on nuclear arms control.

A more personal and detailed account of Pief's life and prodigious achievements can be found in the book he dictated to his secretary in 2006, a year before he died: "Panofsky on Physics, Politics and Peace: Pief remembers." I was asked by the APS to write a review of the book which can be found in Appendix 1.

The lab was administratively organized into four divisions: the Technical Division for the accelerator under Richard Neal, the Research Division for all the particle research under Joseph Ballam, the Business Services Division under Fred Pindar and Eugene Rickansrud, and the Administrative Services Division for Personnel and Publications under Robert Moulton with Gerry Renner, Bill Kirk and Doug Dupen, the latter two being excellent writers.

It should also be mentioned here that for financial and practical reasons, our accelerator location that had originally been planned under the Stanford golf course, was moved to the new site along Sand Hill Road in Menlo Park.

Chapter 5

SLAC construction, turn-on, and early operation (1962-1969)

Construction started in 1962, by which time our staff had to grow by leaps and bounds. Shown below is the first stretch of the accelerator housing in 1963 (Fig. 42).

42

By 1962 I had finished the design of the accelerator structure and I was put in charge of the design and construction of the two-mile klystron drive and phasing systems. With my colleague Ruddy Larsen, I also designed the structures for radio frequency separators whose higher mode traveling-wave fields could push synchronous electrons or other particles transversely rather than longitudinally. These structures were also tested successfully in the Mark IV linear accelerator.

In September 1963 the bi-annual international accelerator conference was held in Dubna, USSR for the first time and about six of us from SLAC were invited to attend. It was an unforgettable experience, from both the scientific and human/political points of view and coincided with the signing of the US-USSR Partial Nuclear Test Ban Treaty in the atmosphere that was a huge relief in the Cold War. As can be imagined, we had many interesting conversations with our Russian colleagues, many of them during walks in the woods around Dubna. Before leaving home, I had taken some rudimentary Russian lessons with a Russian lady in Palo Alto, and this was generally appreciated by our hosts.

43

You can see Pief Panofsky (in white shirt) at Dubna Conference delivering the talk about SLAC, translated by maverick Sergei Kapitsa, standing next to him (Fig. 43).

At the conference I gave a well-received talk about the rf separator we had just built at SLAC, and this explains the next picture where five of us are seen on a boat on the Volga (Fig. 44).

44

Seen from left to right: Unknown, me, Pierre Lapostolle (Saclay), Brian Montague (CERN), and Igor Semenyushkin (Dubna).

After the conference, we spent three very interesting days in Moscow where we saw a magnificent performance of Swan Lake with sensational ballerina Yelena Riabinkina at the Bolshoi Theater, seen below (Fig. 45).

45

Years later with Gilda, I had the pleasure of seeing and greeting Yelena after her performance at the San Francisco Opera. I was very happy because she remembered meeting me in Moscow. It was good for my ego.

With Richard Neal we then traveled to see a medium-size linear electron accelerator run by Professor Grishaev in Kharkov, Ukraine (then a Soviet Republic), and the large Komar Institute in Leningrad. At that institute, we visited various labs and gathered with a bunch of accelerator scientists. It was funny that at one point, I heard Komar (our host) say to one of his staff while pointing at me "Watch out what you say, this guy speaks Russian." I wish! The rest of our Leningrad experience was crowned by visiting the city and, above all, the formidable Hermitage Museum.

We exited Russia via Finland. At the border, the Russian inspectors checked our suitcases thoroughly. At the hotel in Helsinki, Richard and I, finally somewhat more relaxed, enjoyed a fabulous sauna and a huge smorgasbord!

While I was in Russia, the first building to be completed at SLAC was the Test Lab, and my department as well as all my belongings were moved to our nice new offices on the second floor where I would stay until the year 1999.

By now, our staff had grown to about 1400, and construction was proceeding at a frantic pace. Panofsky had chosen the exact linear trajectory to minimize the number of oak trees that would have to be sacrificed (Fig. 46).

As shown upper right, the accelerator was installed in a shielded housing underground. All the 240 klystrons and associated equipment were located 40 ft apart in a gallery above ground, where people could work on a daily basis. The 2856 MHz power from the klystrons feeding the accelerator below was transmitted through vertical shafts by rectangular waveguides (Fig. 47).

The first contingent of 240 klystrons was built by Litton,

46

47

RCA, Sperry, Eimac and SLAC under the supervision of Jean Lebacqz (Fig. 48). The high operating cost of the klystrons was going to be a problem, but their failure rate, due to electron gun and ceramic output window damage, could fortunately be reduced gradually from hundreds to thousands of hours.

The accelerator housing, ten meters underground for radiation shielding, is shown here with John Seeman standing by (several years later) (Fig. 49). Four accelerator sections are mounted on a forty-foot-long aluminum girder, two feet in diameter.

Inside, each girder is equipped with a Fresnel lens that can be flipped into the vertical plane with a piston. A laser located at the East end of the two-mile accelerator, creates an image of the lens on a screen located in the housing at the West end. The position of the image indicates whether every one of 240 forty-foot girders is properly aligned or needs to be adjusted. Given the stability of the concrete housing, such adjustments were rarely needed, except for example in 1989 after the Loma Linda earthquake.

Around 1964, Panofsky also made the decision to create a separate SLAC Faculty to attract first-class particle physicists to head future experiments. This decision created some tension with the existing Stanford Physics Department, but it was very successful in bringing many excellent people to the lab. Among them would be Joe Ballam (hired earlier), Ricard Taylor, David Ritson, Bob Mozley, Martin Perl, Burton Richter, Mel Schwartz, Elliott Bloom, David Leith and others.

During our four-year long construction period, we had a few snags of which I will recount only two. The most threatening one was the power line crisis. We started out with a 60 KV line that could only deliver about 20 MW to our plant. But to cover all our current and future needs, we wanted to insure a maximum availability of up to 80 MW. For this, our power company, PG&E, needed to install 220 KV transmission lines connected from their existing ones on Skyline down to our on-site substation. When the town of Woodside found out that this 220 KV system would entail huge ugly towers and cables coming through their bucolic green environment, they became very upset. They hired a famous lawyer, Pete McCloskey, who took their protest all the way to Ladybird Johnson in the White House. For a while, it looked like that this obstacle would be a showstopper. Fortunately, some clever engineers came up with the design of some much smaller green poles that would blend discreetly into the Woodside landscape. The crisis was resolved!

Pete McCloskey, who had served with the Marines in the Korean War, would be elected slightly later as our very respected local Congressman, courageously opposing the Vietnam War.

The second snag I want to recount was actually a bonus. At the East End of the two-mile accelerator, we needed to excavate a wide area to be able to switch our electron beam from one experiment to the other. This area was called the beam switchyard seen below (Fig. 50). During the excavation the workers suddenly noticed a strange discoloration in the earth and they called their supervisor for advice. Wisely, he called a geologist who identified that there was a large fossil in the ground that should not be damaged. What they had discovered was a large mammal called a Paleoparadoxia because it can live in both the ocean and on land, with feet with fins. The area where we were excavating had been under water during prehistoric times and the mammal was 14 million years old. Within a few days, the entire very rarely found skeleton was safely removed, and excavation could resume. We had discovered our very first big new "particle!"

50

51

Pief Panofsky's wife, Adele, who had some training, spent about twenty years reconstructing the entire animal seen with her above (Fig. 51).

In September 1965 I attended the International Accelerator Conference at Frascati near Rome, Italy where they had built and tested the first successful electron-positron collider storage ring, ADA, with a center-of-mass energy of 500 MeV. A few years later, Frascati built a bigger storage ring called ADONE under the able management of Fernando Amman. By bad luck, they just missed the energy necessary to produce the J/psi!

By Spring of 1966, construction of the accelerator, the switchyard and the large concrete experimental end-stations A and B was completed.

Note, however, that Freeway 280, to run over the accelerator, had not yet been built (Fig. 52).

In the meantime, my responsibilities at SLAC had grown substantially, and I was now head of the Accelerator Physics Department, with about one hundred engineers, physicists and technicians reporting to me. Charlie Kruse was my budget assistant. Roger Miller was head of the Injection Group, Harry Hogg

52

of the Microwave Group, Bill Herrmannsfeldt of Alignment, and Ken Mallory of Instrumentation and Control.

On April 21st, 1966, I had the honor of being put in charge with my colleague Vic Waithman of the turn-on of the first 20 sectors of the machine.

It would be a glorious hard-day's night, shown in two stages in the photos to the right (Figs. 53 & 54).

In the second picture, (doctored up as happy Beatles by photographer Walter Zawojsky) in the foreground from left to right you can see Pief Panofsky with a guitar, Matt Sands, myself, Richard Neal, Dieter Walz, Ed Seppi, and Ken Crook.

The full 30-sector machine was tested a month later, on May 16/17th, which prompted Panofsky to send his announcement to the full staff, shown on page 76 (Fig. 55).

We had indeed completed the construction of the machine within schedule and budget, but shortly thereafter, we discovered that one of our specifications could not be met. The linear accelerator had successfully reached 16 GeV in beam energy and was pulsing at the design repetition rate of 360 pulses per second, each 2.5 microseconds long. But the beam 1.6 micro-

74 GREGORY A. LOEW

THE BEAM IS STUCK IN SECTOR II

THE BEAM HITS SECTOR 20!

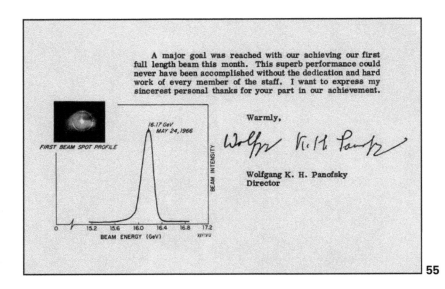

A major goal was reached with our achieving our first full length beam this month. This superb performance could never have been accomplished without the dedication and hard work of every member of the staff. I want to express my sincerest personal thanks for your part in our achievement.

Warmly,

Wolfgang K. H. Panofsky

Wolfgang K. H. Panofsky
Director

FIRST BEAM SPOT PROFILE

16.17 GeV
MAY 24, 1966

BEAM INTENSITY

0   15.2   15.6   16.0   16.4   16.8   17.2
BEAM ENERGY (GeV)

55

seconds current pulse which was supposed to reach 50 milliamperes, couldn't get to the end of the accelerator above 15 milliamperes. At first, the cause of this limitation was not at all obvious, and it took about a month and some of the best accelerator theorists like Pief Panofsky (with Postdoc Myron Bander) and Richard Helm to find the explanation. What was happening was that the 960 sections of the accelerator were cumulatively amplifying a signal arising from noise in the beam starting from the front-end injector. The microwave mode that parasitically resonated at 4140 MHz was the same as I had used in my rf separators, but its detrimental effect was that beyond a certain beam pulse length or amplitude (15 milliamperes), the electrons were deflected transversely. This caused the round beam pulse to gradually break up into a wide stripe before it reached the end of the machine. Accordingly, we called the effect "beam break up" or BBU for short.

Once we had understood the theoretical explanation of the phenomenon, we spent a couple of months studying it experimentally to see what we could do to remediate it. Two practical solutions arose. One was to redeploy the ninety quadrupole focusing magnets of the machine in a more efficient way to keep the cross-section of the beam from growing. The second was to retune the front-end of each ten-foot accelerator section so that the amplification of the 4140 MHz mode that resonated there would be selectively detuned by 2 or 4 MHz with an external" dimpling" tool. We calculated that together, these separate approaches would easily get us to the desired 50 milliampere specification. However, to effect these cures, it was necessary to enter the machine housing, and the particle physicists who were all happy to start their experiments with 15 milliamperes of electrons, wanted us to deliver their beams immediately. We thus compromised and took about three years to gradually fix the entire accelerator to our total satisfaction. By about 1970, our current was up to 80 milliamperes!

The fact that the linear accelerator could produce 360 beam pulses per second meant that several experiments could run in parallel in End-Stations A, B, and C. Pleasing all the users simultaneously was a great challenge for us, machine physicists and operators, particularly since their demands were all different, and they were all impatient.

Two of these experiments consisted of bombarding protons in pure hydrogen with electrons. One was a 40 in. hydrogen bubble chamber in End-Station C whose pressure could be reduced for a very short time to allow particles produced inside to form visible bubble tracks, as shown in the photograph next page top (Fig. 56). The curvature of the tracks resulting from a external transverse magnetic field enabled professionals to identify and measure the energy of these particles. The larger the curvature, the higher the energy. Tens of thousands of these pictures were taken and analyzed.

The other technique, pursued in End Station A by builders Richard Taylor from SLAC, and Jerome Friedmann and Henry Kendall from M.I.T., also used hydrogen targets but in a much

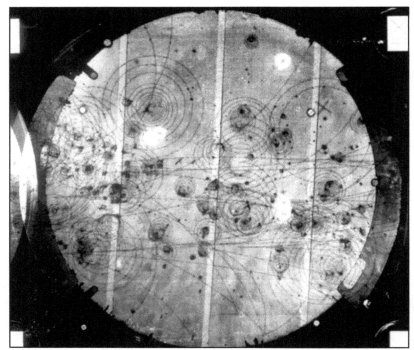

56

smaller vessel located at the fulcrum of some large magnetic spectrometers capable of detecting and counting the electrons scattered by the protons in the target, as a function of angle and energy, as shown below. Notice the rails on the ground over which the spectrometers could be rotated.

It is important to note that for the first couple of years, these spectrometer experiments were done by measuring *elastic electron scattering* (in which the total kinetic energy of the electron plus that of the proton before and after the collision does not change), and no surprising results were found. These elastic experiments were also checked with 12 GeV positrons (anti-electrons with positive charge) created at the end of sector 11, with no different results either,

In addition, there were photoproduction experiments in ESA (using photon beams generated by electrons on targets), a streamer chamber in ESC, and a spark chamber in ESB.

detector-install.jpg **57**

In early 1967, the SLAC Directorate had a long discussion about how to preserve all the scientific and engineering information that had gone into the planning, design and construction of the accelerator, the beam switchyard, and the early experimental areas. The conclusion of these discussions was to ask Richard Neal to lead the effort to produce a book that would accomplish this.

Neal in turn formed an editorial committee consisting of Harry Hogg, Doug Dupen and myself to take on the task. We divided the book into twenty-seven chapters and assigned each chapter to an editor with about 150 of my memorable colleagues of the time. We met for about nine months at 8:00 am for an hour to go through the voluminous material. It was a daunting task, but also very rewarding because all the information was well recorded in one place. The final result was the publication of The Stanford Two-Mile Accelerator by W.A. Benjamin, Inc. in 1968.

Shortly thereafter, Neal and I were invited to contribute to a general book on linear accelerators by Lapostolle and Septier to be published in Paris.

In September 1969, three weeks after my marriage to Gilda, the International Accelerator Conference was held in Armenia, and we combined the trip with our later honeymoon in Sicily. At the conference which started in Yerevan and continued in the mountain resort at Tsakadzor where Soviet Olympic competitors had trained for the altitude of Mexico City, I reported in detail on our experience with BBU, which for accelerator physicists was very intriguing. We were also taken on some very interesting excursions in Armenia like Etchmiadzin, and one place where we could see Mount Ararat in Turkey. We also met scientist Sam Kheifetz and his wife Julia who later would emigrate to the U.S. Gilda was totally fascinated by all our experiences in the Soviet Union. Here she is seen dealing with a private entrepreneur on the street (Fig. 58).

58

Of course, Sicily with its magnificent ruins was fabulous too.

1969 was also the year when Fermi National Accelerator Laboratory was founded by director Robert R. Wilson, with his high-rise hall shown below (Fig. 60).

59

60

Chapter 6

A President visits SLAC (1970)

By 1970, SLAC was beginning to be well known in the world scientific community, and I had my first experience with a head of state. Many French visitors had already visited the lab and I was often invited with them by the French Consul in San Francisco, Monsieur Batault. Sometime in January, he called me and told me that President Georges Pompidou planned to visit the U.S. in February and was very interested to come to SLAC after seeing NASA at Cape Kennedy. Would that be possible? I immediately informed Pief Panofsky who was very pleased by the news and told me to organize the entire event.

The whole experience was a huge challenge for me on many fronts. The President would arrive at the Fairmont Hotel the night before, and there would be no time to drive him back and forth along the 101 Freeway, so it was decided that I would fetch him and his entourage at the Fairmont and make the two trips by helicopter from the heliport at the Presidio. As it turned out, he traveled with Foreign Minister Maurice Schumann, the French Scientific Attaché in Washington D.C. and several other French diplomats. It would take two helicopters! All kinds of other people had to be involved, the Chief of Protocol of San Francisco, the Board of Trustees of the University, members of the Faculty and others. To complicate matters even more, several Jewish organizations in the area had discovered that France had recently sold Mirage planes to Libya, and they wanted to protest Pompidou's visit. I had to negotiate with them to allow them to come to our site, but not too close to the President. All of this took hours of attention and planning. In the end, the event on February 27th worked out flawlessly, except for the fact that the President and his Foreign Minister came down in different elevators in the Fairmont (contrary to plans) and we almost missed the President. The Jewish organizers held signs saying "Peace is not a mirage" but the two helicopters landed without problems.

You can enjoy the pictures following, the helicopter landing with the demonstrators in back (Fig. 61), Panofsky lecturing and me translating (Figs. 62 & 63), CERN Director General Victor Weisskopf attending (Fig. 64), the President (Fig. 65) and Congressman Pete McCloskey talking (Fig. 66).

After his visit to SLAC, President Pompidou returned to San Francisco and the Fairmont Hotel where he and his wife Claude had a short meeting with then Governor Ronald Reagan and his wife Nancy. He then gave a luncheon speech about French policy toward the European Union.

In the summer of 1970, the President found out that I was

61

62

63

spending a vacation in Paris, and he invited me for a fifteen-minute meeting with him at the Elysée Palace. During our conversation, he asked me why he was reading about so many riots in the U.S., and I told him that most of them were protests

 64

 65

 66

against the continuing Vietnam War.

About two years later, French Ambasssador de Laboulaye, grandson of the man who promoted the gift of the Statue of Liberty, decorated me with the French *Ordre du Mérite*.

CHAPTER 7

The complicated saga of the first three quarks (1961-1971)

The discovery of the first real quarks at SLAC did not happen overnight. To understand what happened, we must step back to the beginning of the 1960s. At this time, the state of particle physics was in disarray: more than one hundred separate particles had been identified. This, to our desire for mental reductionism, made the idea that they were all "fundamental" unpalatable.

In 1961 Caltech physicist Murray Gell-Mann came up with a classification he called the Eight-Fold Way that put some order into this complex picture. Then, in 1964, he and George Zweig independently proposed mathematical models based on three "sub-particles" called "u, d and s quarks" [and their anti-quarks] which in various combinations of 2 or 3 made up all the other observed particles. Their electric charges were 1/3 or 2/3 of the electron charge. Because of their explanatory power, these models were very convincing but did not imply that the quarks could ever be observed experimentally. Richard Feynman came up with yet a different model of parton constituents, but still without experimental verification.

As mentioned earlier, the *elastic scattering* of electrons on protons did not seem to reveal any substructure, in particular the scattering cross-section fell off sharply as a function of the transfer of momentum, similarly to billiard balls. However, when the electron energy was increased, the electrons could penetrate inside the proton and *inelastic scattering* was observed: the internal structure of the proton revealed a phenomenon called *scaling*, proposed by SLAC theorist James Bjorken in 1968. After three more years of head scratching, this observation could only be explained by the idea that the proton was not a single homogeneous jelly-like blob, but indeed contained three seed-like scattering quarks – two "up" and one "down", just as Gell-Mann had predicted.

This discovery was a huge achievement. It ushered the field into what is now called the Standard Model of Particle Physics.

The Standard Model can be represented by the cubic structure shown in its incomplete form below (Fig. 67): three pink-colored **strongly** interacting quarks, four **weakly** interacting greenish-looking leptons below, and so far, only one bluish-colored force carrier, the gamma ray. The gluon, strong force carrier between the quarks, was discovered a few years later at DESY.

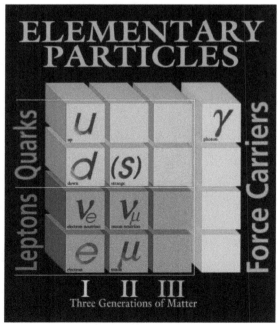

67

Richard Taylor (see below, Fig. 68), Jerome Friedmann and Henry Kendall received the Physics Nobel Prize in 1990, and James Bjorken received the Wolf Prize in 2015.

68

Chapter 8

SLED and SPEAR

Pief Panofsky always said that the only way SLAC would survive would be if it could find a major way to renew itself every ten years or so.

That indeed is what happened in 1970 with two innovations.

The first one took a while to materialize. SLAC had initially been built with the possibility of doubling the beam energy by quadrupling the number of klystrons and their modulators to 960, i.e. one klystron per accelerator section. When we looked into this scheme, we realized that it would be far too costly and energy intensive. One alternative that was being investigated at HEPL on campus was to convert the copper accelerator sections to superconducting lead or niobium sections with higher electric gradient. The HEPL scientists were competent but overoptimistic, and one of them, Perry Wilson, moved to SLAC to work with me. With a staff of about ten people, we tried for two years to come up with niobium cavities that could support electric fields of 30 megavolts per meter that might have yielded a continuous beam of 100 GeV. Unfortunately, we found out that the technology was far from ready, and the superconducting project was abandoned. After another year of studying another possibility of recirculating the existing 20 GeV beam twice through the accelerator, we also had to abandon this project because of its complexity and cost.

Necessity being the mother of invention, Harry Hogg, Perry

Wilson, and David Farkas finally came up with the idea eventually called SLAC Energy Development or SLED. The idea was to store the energy of each klystron pulse in an intermediate pair of large copper cavities, and after about half the pulse, let it be added to the second half, and be discharged into the accelerator. If implemented for all 240 klystrons, this clever scheme could at first increase the SLAC beam energy to 30 GeV. The cost would be about $10K per klystron but it could be implemented gradually over 5 years or so by being absorbed by our operating budget. This is exactly what was done.

A picture of one SLED cavity pair, with from left to right, Perry Wilson, me, Harry Hogg and David Farkas, is shown below (Fig. 69).

69

The second innovation was also a while in coming. When he came from MIT to Stanford, Burt Richter decided to do a test of electromagnetism by colliding electrons against electrons in two adjacent rings at the end of the HEPL linear accelerator. The rings worked fine, and this inspired Burt to propose an electron-positron collider at SLAC, Unfortunately the two rings cost about $10 M and he could not find the money, particularly because he could not tell anybody what he would find with it. He tried for almost ten years until 1970 when Panofsky told him to greatly simplify the design into a single ring to store both particles, and to reduce the cost to $4M which Panofsky would fund with in-house equipment money. Burt complied and in a little more than two years, built the Stanford Positron Electron Asymmetric Ring, or SPEAR, shown below (Fig. 70) on a concrete pad at the end of the SLAC accelerator. Up to 2.5 GeV electros and positrons could be made available, injected tangentially and stored to collide head-on.

70

For two years electrons and positrons successfully collided head-on over a range of equal energies but nothing exciting happened, until one night in November 1974, they hit the jackpot with a very careful scan around 3.1 GeV in the center-of-mass. At this energy, they had found a natural new resonant state labeled Psi consisting of two charm quarks, one c quark and one anti-c quark. This was the kind of event that most particle physicists can only dream of. Two years later, Burt Richter was awarded the1976 Physics Nobel Prize for coming up with the storage ring and detector, the Mark I, where the discovery was made. As it turns out, he shared the prize with Sam Ting who had almost simultaneously discovered the same resonance (he called J) with protons at Brookhaven National Laboratory. The resonance for this reason is called the J/Psi.

In 1975-1976, SLAC's Martin Perl, with a more painstaking search on the same machine, found what is the third lepton, after the electron and the muon, called the tau. For this discovery, Perl would earn the 1995 Physics Nobel Prize. With these two

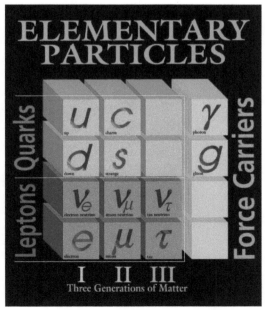

71

discoveries and that of the gluons that bind the quarks, at DESY, the Standard Model had now grown as shown (Fig. 71).

Meanwhile in 1973, another momentous discovery had been made at SPEAR, principally by Ed Garwin and Gerry Fischer: **synchrotron radiation.** By rotating around the storage ring, electrons and positrons were constantly emitting ultra-violet and X-rays tangentially to their orbits, and this radiation could be extracted through windows in the vacuum chamber and used for a large variety of physical, chemical, and biological research. An entirely new technology had been invented, that would be used for years to come with storage rings and free electron lasers all over the world. The synchrotron radiation project at SPEAR would be run by SSRL under university management. More details on SSRL can be found in Chapter 16.

The huge success with SPEAR gave physicists the incentive to propose and build a much larger ring at SLAC in collaboration with LBNL. This storage ring that would collide 15 GeV electrons against 15 GeV positrons was called PEP. It was completed in 1980 and ran for about five years. It was equipped with six interaction regions and five detectors. One of its main discoveries was that the b quark that was produced in pairs as a B particle at about 10 GeV had a long lifetime. This property would give birth twenty years later to the B Factory project.

Chapter 9

Other diverse activities (1974-1981)

During this period, I worked on several other projects.

One had to do with the energy loss of a single electron bunch as it passes through our entire linear accelerator. Calculations were hard to make, so I proposed to try to measure the effect experimentally. This required installing some special equipment in the injector up front, and for this I was ably assisted by Roger Miller and Ron Koontz who was doing his PhD under him and me. The challenge was to generate and launch a single bunch of adjustable intensity (total charge) but constant shape and aspect ratio. This they did with four different insertable sieves of identical cross-section but different number of holes. The difference in total energy loss could be measured in the beam switchyard spectrum analyzer. It was a spectacular experiment, and it gave us a result that we could trust.

Another project was triggered by a request from Stanford Medical School Professor Henry Kaplan, the chief radiologist. Kaplan knew that unlike with electron therapy, the use of negative pi mesons allowed one to avoid radiation damage of healthy tissue on the way to the tumor to be destroyed. This was the case because the negative pions only cause damage where they explode locally in the form of little stars. The depth in the tissue depends just on the energy of the incident pions.

I was asked to design an electron linear accelerator capable of producing enough pions on a target from which the pions could be focused on the patients. Such a focusing system had already been designed at HEPL at Stanford. This project occupied me and my colleague Dieter Walz at SLAC part-time for a few months. We came up with a design and cost estimate (~$12M) that Kaplan submitted to the NIH. The NIH liked the design but was intimidated by the cost that would have been hard to reduce to make it competitive on a national scale. In the end, we were thanked for our pro-bono work but turned down.

A third project that I became involved in was a system by which to produce a continuous beam of 3-6 GeV electrons to do high-precision nuclear physics experiments. My proposal, submitted to the University of Virginia, was an electron linear accelerator combined with a circular pulse stretcher from which one could gradually "peel off" a constant stream of electrons. My proposal was very competitive with other proposals, and it was accepted as the best placeholder for a national machine to be built in Virginia. As it happened, Hermann Grunder from Argonne National Laboratory was named director of the project at a time when superconducting linear accelerators were finally making some encouraging progress. Based on this, he decided to give this technology a chance. It took many more years to bring this project to fruition at Thomas Jefferson Lab in Newport News, but in retrospect, it was a good choice because it gave a huge boost to superconducting linear accelerators. Indirectly, I had done my part.

Chapter 10

Two weeks in the People's Republic of China (1979)

In September 1979, with the gradual opening of China to the West, six of us from Stanford and SLAC were invited to give some lectures on accelerators in Beijing and in Hofei. This trip was one of the most interesting experiences of my life. We first flew from San Frncisco to Hong Kong where we spent a couple of days, before entering China by train to Guangzhou.

72

Seen from left to right: Phil and Arlene Morton, Rosalyn and Art Bienenstock, Ben and wife Salzberg, Renee and Hermann Winick in Hong Kong (Fig. 72).

Mao Zedong had died in 1976, ten years after the beginning of the Cultural Revolution. The Gang of Four, including Mao's wife, had been incarcerated shortly thereafter. Wherever we were invited, our hosts first introduced us to the new regime that followed the "terrible times of the Cultural Revolution" but the population was still living in a controlled Communist state under Hua Guofeng. Everybody was wearing a blue Mao jacket and riding a bicycle, hauling some vegetables on their racks. In Beijing, we were taken to a large popular celebration with hand-held card shows (Fig. 73).

Privately I was taken to Democracy Wall in a park which was much less advertised, mostly against the Gang of Four (Figs. 74, 75).

73

74

75

We were also taken to other great sights like the Great Wall (Fig. 76), the Forbidden City (Fig. 77), the fabulous Summer Palace (Fig. 78) and the Ming Tombs (Fig. 79) where they wanted to build a huge dam and a proton accelerator, neither of which materialized.

76

77

78

79

After giving a couple of lectures at the Nuclear Physics Institute in Beijing, we were flown to Hofei where they were about to build a synchrotron light facility, and we would spend a full week with a large group of students, some of them seen next page upper right (Fig. 80) as well as Juwen Wang, the excellent student from Tsinghua University, who would join me at SLAC a year later.

80

What was so amazing in Hofei was to see how a third-world country was pulling itself up by its bootstraps with the most strenuous manual labor shown below (Figs. 81 and 82).

One day, a whole bunch of people approached us on the street "*en masse*" and asked us about JFK and Nixon. When we told them we didn't have a good opinion of the latter, they were very disappointed: "Why? He made peace with us, he was wonderful!"

81

82

Another opportunity we were given while in Hofei was to visit a nearby farm cooperative, very typical of China at that time.

As seen below (Fig. 83), the living quarters of the farmers were very primitive, without running water nor electricity. Cooking was done with dry straw. The one-child policy had not yet reached the countryside, and the farmer, through an interpreter, let us know that he had raised four kids in his house.

83

When we left the coop, children were just getting out of school. They had never seen white people in their lifetime, and they all wanted to touch us. Our guide, after a few minutes, had to rescue us from them (Fig. 84).

84

After Hofei, we spent a couple of days in Shanghai, where again, people mobbed us on the street as if we came from Mars. The overpopulation in Shanghai was overwhelming.

We left China after these incredible two weeks, again via Hong Kong (Fig. 85).

85

Chapter 11

The era of the Stanford Linear Collider and the Z particle (1981-1998)

This era was probably the most complicated and tumultuous of our lab's existence.

Around 1978 Burt Richter had spent a sabbatical year at CERN and he had convinced his colleagues there that they should build a 27 km electron-positron storage ring to explore the properties of the Z particle that Carlo Rubbia had discovered in 1976 at their Super Proton Storage Ring. This machine would be known as LEP, the Large Electron Positron Project. However, when Burt came home, he thought that SLAC should build a competing collider. The problem was that SLAC did not have enough real estate to build such a machine, and another invention was needed. After a year or so, he came up with the Stanford Linear Collider or SLC. The basic idea was to accelerate an electron beam and a positron beam in two collinear machines facing each other and let them collide at a common focus. The challenge at SLAC was that we had only one linear accelerator, so we had to invent a system to use it for both particles.

The SLC ended up looking like the schematic drawn to scale seen next page top (Fig. 86). Several innovations had to

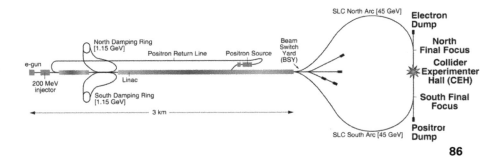

86

be made: 1) the creation of three massive single bunches of 50 billion particles each at the East-End injector, 2) the creation of a new positron source in Sector 20 in which one electron bunch would create a positron bunch returning to the front-end to get damped, 3) two damping rings at the front end to make the electron and (returning) positrons as small as possible, 4) a two-mile accelerator capable of bringing two bunches to about 46 GeV each to produce the ~92 GeV Z particle, 5) two arcs with appropriate bending and focusing magnets to bring the two bunches into collision, 6) a final focus to bring the two bunches to a micron-size cross section, and 7) a detector to measure the properties of the Z particles produced.

The design of the entire system would take until 1983 when Richter obtained about $112 Million from the DOE to build it. Preceding these good news, two unpleasant developments took place that year.

The first was that Richard Neal (65) stepped down as director of the Technical Division in 1983 and left SLAC in 1985. He was first replaced by Burt Richter, and a year later by Kaye Lathrop from Los Alamos National Laboratory. Unfortunately, Lathrop had no accelerator experience and was very authoritarian. After ten years, he left and was replaced by very able Ewan Paterson.

The second one, that led to a major controversy at SLAC, was triggered by a proposal by Lawrence Livermore National Laboratory (LLNL) to conduct some nuclear weapons related research at SSRL. The work would consist of testing and calibrating instruments for the Edward Teller proposed nuclear "Star Wars" space-based anti-ballistic missile. This was an X-ray laser, which was supported by the Reagan Administration but was unlikely to work. Arthur Bienenstock, Director of SSRL, had received the proposal and as the SLAC Faculty and staff became aware of it, a strong reaction against participating in this research emerged: 15 Faculty (including myself) and 280 staff (led by Mary James) signed a petition and submitted it to SLAC and University management. It asked that the proposal be rejected because of its end-use, even though it would not be "classified". SLAC Director Pief Panofsky was not favorable to the work but could not see how he could prevent it since SSRL was NOT under his management, but under direct university management. Faculty and staff countered that helping with these experiments was tantamount to "involuntary servitude." Furthermore, it would tarnish the peaceful image of SLAC where many people worked under the assumption that there was no weapons-related work. The conflict festered for weeks, but eventually Art Bienenstock, fully supported by Stanford President Donald Kennedy, decided to approve the project simply because it was unclassified. This was a big defeat for the SLAC opponents. However, it turned out that months later, LLNL that was going to install the beam lines for the work at SSRL decided not to do the research at SLAC, and the entire controversy was defused. For a more detailed discussion of this issue, see Appendix 2.

Back to the SLC:

Once the construction of the SLC started and gradual commissioning followed, accelerator specialists in Japan, at DESY in Hamburg, and at CERN were inspired by the SLC and began to design higher energy linear collider projects of their own, possibly to discover the Higgs boson. This development led to new collaborations, particularly between SLAC and KEK in Tsukuba, Japan. Mutual visits and exchanges became very frequent. I went to Japan for the first time in 1984 to give lectures at a winter school on Mount Fuji, and to visit klystron manufacturers at Toshiba and Mitsubishi.

Starting that year, I also began to participate in annual international conferences and collaborations with labs like BEPC in China, CERN, Russia, South Korea, and Latin America. In Beijing, thanks to T.D. Lee, we met with the Prime Minister twice. I also became personally very involved in the design of the much larger linear collider capable of discovering the Higgs particle, mentioned above.

Pief Panofsky (65) stepped down as SLAC Director in 1985 but stayed at the lab until the last day of his life in 2007. He was replaced by Burt Richter who now had to run the lab as well as to commission the SLC.

Reaching 46 GeV per beam took a major effort. The new specified klystron of 50 MW peak power with a 5 microsecond pulse was hard to build. Both its gun and single ceramic output window were failing. In the end the gun breakdown was solved by going to a higher peak power of 64 MW and a shorter ~4.5 microsecond pulse. The window problem was circumvented by installing two parallel vertical ceramic windows so that dust (whose discharge produced the ceramic punctures) would fall to the edge where the rf fields were too low to make trouble! Two or three years later, equipped with the existing SLED cavities and 240 new klystrons, the linac was able to produce 46 GeV electron and positron beams, enough to reach the Z-mass in collision! The higher average klystron power, however, made us reduce the machine repetition rate from 360 to 120 pulses per second. The new klystron can be seen on the nest page (Fig. 87).

87

The damping rings probably took two years to commission. But the two arcs (see construction below Fig. 88) and the final foci were the most difficult to make work.

88

One of Richter's assistants on the SLC, a smart but too much of a wise guy, had to be fired. Fortunately, he was replaced by Nan Phinney who saved the project through her sound judgment and technical expertise. The first Z particles were recorded in 1989 by the Mark II detector brought by Jonathan Dorfan from PEP. The second detector, built under the management of Martin Breidenbach, was the SLD shown below (Fig. 89) with its entire research staff:

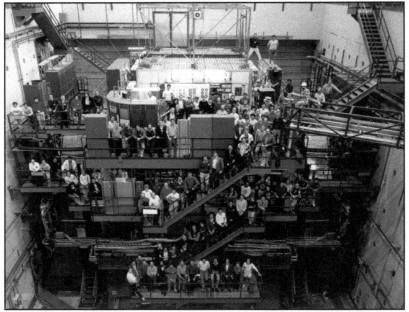

89

The SLC ran for about ten years. It produced about 350,000 Z particles which pinned down the Z's exact mass and showed from their decay width that there were only three neutrino families. By the way, LEP confirmed all these results. The SLC also made a seminal measurement of the so-called Weinberg angle with polarized electrons.

By this time, the SLAC campus looked a lot more complicated, as shown on the next page (Fig. 90) with the SLC and PEP, soon to become PEP II. You can now see the Standard Model of

Particle Physics, almost complete with bottom and top quarks discovered at Fermilab, the gluon at DESY and the W and Z bosons at CERN (Fig. 91).

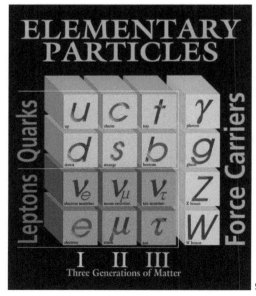

Chapter 12

Juwen Wang, Electric Power, Arms Control, the SSC, the Tigers, and a Shoot-out (1980-1995)

Less than a year after my trip to China, Juwen Wang, thanks to a Chinese scholarship he obtained through his Tsinghua University professor Liu Naichuan, arrived at SLAC in 1980 to study with me. The marvelous relationship we established is fully described in the next chapter.

During the last two years of Richard Neal's leadership (1981-1983), I became his Division Deputy and began to help him with some of his responsibilities concerning the acquisition and administration of electric power needed for the lab. This activity, which is described from its origins in Chapter 18 stayed under my supervision for the next twenty-five years, was very interesting for me in that it opened my eyes to a large sector of the economy.

At this point in my career, my academic title had changed from Adjunct Professor to Professor of Applied Research, and in addition to my seminars on the Causes of War, I occasionally also taught a graduate course on accelerators in the Stanford Department of Applied Physics.

Meanwhile, Stanford had also organized an active group involved in Arms Control, and I regularly attended their luncheon lectures delivered by Stanford and nationwide specialists. One of the Stanford Junior Professors who often sat across the table from me was the likable Condoleezza Rice (actually called Condolcezza by her father). For reasons I cannot explain, she was then a very different person from the one she became in the Bush Administration twenty years later. These Arms Control lectures helped me significantly for my seminars on war.

1984 was also the year when the Superconducting Super Collider or SSC got a big boost from the HEP community and the U.S. government. Approval of this gigantic 40 TeV center-of-mass energy proton-proton collider in Waxahachie, Texas didn't materialize until 1989, and construction began in 1990. I could have joined the project, but given its fate in 1993, I was lucky I didn't. I did however visit the site several times to advise their staff on how to optimize their electric power contracts with the local power companies. If I remember correctly, the project needed about 100 MW of power, more than any accelerator complex in the past, and this alone was a daunting task. For a multitude of complicated financial and political reasons, the SSC was cancelled in 1993, after spending its first $2 Billion.

Ironically, the site had acquired about $1 Billion of disposable equipment and supplies, and the DOE was asked to come up with a fair system to distribute all these wares to other U.S. labs that could make good use of them. The Office of Science came up with the highly respected Earle Fowler to take charge of this task, and he in turn picked about 7 or 8 scientists to assist him. I was the representative chosen from SLAC. We set up a computer program to help us keep track of all the items and their destinations. This King Solomon job took us two years but it was accomplished fairly and seamlessly. The last two items, the SSC cafeteria furniture and the Expresso machine, went to

SLAC and LBNL respectively.

Another less entertaining side-time job that I got around that time had to do with several visits of the so-called tiger teams. These were people sent from elsewhere specializing in the inspection of work hazards. Like all labs, SLAC had occasional accidents and the DOE wanted us to correct the conditions that caused them. The tiger teams would come for a week or so at a time and make extensive lists of the problems they saw. At some point, the list included hundreds of complaints, and we were asked to draft a complete Corrective Action Plan, listing remedies and costs. SLAC hired a couple of consultants, and I was put in charge of working with them to draft the entire plan. It was exhausting because I had to do this work in addition to all my other normal activities, and it took several months to complete. We were the given a year or two to implement the plan with all its bells and whistles.

Around 1990, as per Panofsky's usual motto of always having a new project in our back-pocket after the SLC, two competing accelerator proposals surfaced at the lab. One was a new stand-alone Tau-Charm Factory proposed by Martin Perl who asked me to design the injector linac for the storage ring. The other one was the B-Factory proposed by Jonathan Dorfan and colleagues to study parity violation in the b-anti b sector. The SLAC Scientific Policy Committee (SPC) knew that we couldn't build both, and a special sub-committee of experts was formed to make the choice by means of a so-called shoot-out. The B-Factory won. Disappointed Martin Perl went to CERN to ask the European Community to build the Tau-Charm Factory, and they in turn suggested that it be built near Seville in Spain. A wealthy Spanish industrialist, owner of the Abengoa Corporation, invited Martin Perl, Rafael Schindler and me to Seville where we spent three days, made detailed presentations to the potential staff, inspected the site, and on the side saw the best

Flamenco dancers I had ever seen. A year later, the more opulent city of Barcelona prevailed over Seville with a proposal to build a synchrotron radiation facility.

Chapter 13

My association with Juwen Wang (1980-Present)

In this chapter I want to describe my wonderful discovery of Juwen Wang.

Juwen Wang was born in Henan Province, China in 1943, in the middle of WW2. In school, he was always an excellent student, and in 1960 at age 17, he was admitted to Tsinghua University. Unfortunately, the Cultural Revolution started in 1966, and he was sent to a factory to build equipment for the Chinese Merchant Marine. He was lucky, however, that at the factory he met Quin, the charming daughter of his boss, and he married her (Fig. 92).

92

After the end of the Cultural Revolution, Juwen was readmitted to Tsinghua University where I met him, studying accelerator physics. As I mentioned earlier, his professor got him a scholarship to come to Stanford where he arrived in 1980, as seen below (Fig. 93).

93

As soon as he came, he proved himself with some calculations and experiments for linear accelerator structures, so much so that by 1982, Professor Chodorow of the Applied Physics Department offered him a scholarship to do his PhD under my guidance at SLAC.

Juwen's thesis turned out to become a valuable tome that covered several important topics of which the most innovative was a comprehensive study of radio frequency breakdown in copper accelerator structures. The high-gradient studies performed in a radiation shielded area in the Cryogenics Lab, demonstrated that the breakdown gradient increased with rf frequency, as tested with sample cavities shown next page top (Fig. 94).

The damage done to the cavities shown next page bottom (Fig. 95) was caused by high electric field gradients that Juwen calculated for radio frequencies from the Fowler-Nordheim formula derived for DC from Quantum Mechanics.

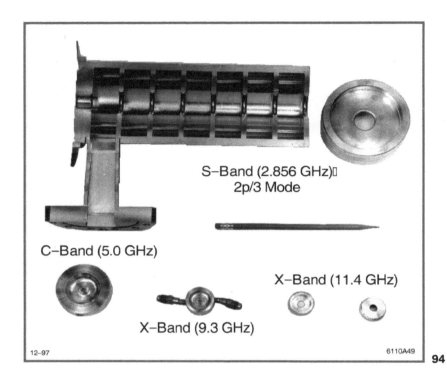

S–Band (2.856 GHz)
2p/3 Mode

C–Band (5.0 GHz)

X–Band (9.3 GHz)

X–Band (11.4 GHz)

12–97   6110A49

94

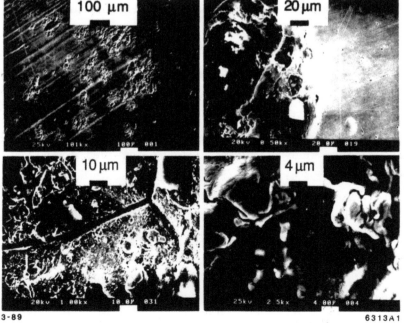

100 μm

20 μm

10 μm

4 μm

3-89   6313A1

95

The damage that appears as craters to the naked eye was found to be more complicated under a microscope. Several years later, it was discovered that the electric field-emission breakdown might be precipitated by magnetic field heating and surface dislocation.

Juwen received his well-deserved PhD from Stanford in 1989 (see Fig. 96), just around the time of the Tiananmen massacre in Beijing. Good thing Juwen and his family were in the U.S. at the time!

96

No sooner had he graduated, Juwen began to work on the development of high-gradient structures at 11.424 GHz (X-band) for future linear room-temperature colliders. This work led him to collaborate with colleagues like Toshi Higo at KEK in Tsukuba, Japan. One of these structures, partially built in Japan, can be seen on the next page in Fig. 97.

In 2009, for all his pioneering work, Juwen was elected to become a fellow of the American Physical Society.

In 2012 Juwen's wife Quin sadly died prematurely, but fortunately he has a wonderful son, daughter-in-law and two grandchildren.

To celebrate Juwen's 70th birthday, Tsinghua University organized a symposium on high-gradient structures in 2013 in

97

Beijing. His brother Juwu and more than fifty scientists from all over the world attended the symposium which ended with a proverbial Chinese banquet and laudatory speeches.

In 2014, Juwen worked on a consulting job at Accuray Corp. for the design of a compact linear electron accelerator for cargo customs inspection, for which he and his colleagues were invited to the White House to receive the Tibbetts award, as shown below in Fig. 98. Juwen is now retired.

98

Chapter 14

The fall of the Soviet Union (1989-1993)

In September 1986, I attended the 13th International Accelerator Conference at BINP in Novosibirsk, Siberia. Mikhail Gorbachev had become General Secretary of the Communist Party of the USSR in 1985 and you could feel that his policies of Glasnost (Openness) and Perestroika (Restructuring) were beginning to have an effect on the atmosphere in the country. After the April 1986 nuclear accident in Chernobyl, near Kiev in Ukraine (then part of the USSR), Gorbachev had convinced himself that reforms were needed in the regime. During our conference banquet, I was fortunate to sit with well-known theorist Lev Okun, and I asked him what he thought about Gorbachev, to which he openly replied: "He is very smart, and you know what, he even got good grades in school, unlike previous leaders!"

In 1988, Gorbachev also became Chairman of the Presidium of the Politburo. By then he had withdrawn all Russian troops from Afghanistan, met with President Reagan, removed all tactical nuclear weapons from Eastern Europe, demoted many corrupt bureaucrats from government positions, restructured domestic elections, and brought Andrei Sakharov out of exile.

By the summer of 1989, spontaneous liberalization movements were taking hold in Poland and Hungary, and increasing pressures were rising in the German Democratic Republic

(Communist East Germany) to allow discontented people to emigrate to West Germany. Gorbachev did not intervene, and the East German government fumbled through a series of gradual concessions that culminated with the fall of the Berlin Wall on November 9th, 1989. This turned out to be one of the most important events of the Cold War, it led to the reunification of Germany, and to the eventual collapse of all communist regimes in Eastern Europe, including the USSR.

Meanwhile, back at home, the SLC at SLAC had collected its first Z particles, and several linear collider designs in the world were making progress, so much so that the 3rd International Linear Collider Workshop was convened to be held in Protvino, Russia in early August 1991. Unfortunately, at the last moment the meeting had to be postponed because of the coup against Gorbachev that lasted for a short time before being defeated. I arrived in Protvino (two hours by car south of Moscow) on September 21st. The meeting was well attended and productive, but too much vodka was served.

During this meeting I was also invited to take a personal tour of three huge local labs and machine shops where they were assembling the upcoming UNK circular proton accelerator (which never got completed). It was a Friday afternoon after lunch and as the very vocal Russian engineer was showing me around, I noticed that all the machine shops were deserted. "How come nobody is working today?" I asked. He looked at me and replied: "The workers take the afternoon off to make more money on private jobs on the side." - "How is this possible, why did your whole system of Communism collapse?" to which he replied: "I think it is because after seventy years, workers finally decided that they'd rather work for themselves than for a corrupt collective system that didn't benefit them!" I guess it was NOT, as some claimed, because the USSR was bankrupted by its expenditures to compete with our Star Wars.

After Protvino, I stopped in Moscow where my friend Nicholas Sobenin from the MIPHI Institute drove me around to see how Communism was rapidly decaying. On Red Square, the statue of Karl Marx had a sign hanging around his neck saying, "Workers of the world, forgive me", and in a park there was a graveyard-like corral with discarded statues of Stalin, Beria, Dzerzhinsky, etc. as seen below (Fig. 99).

99

I finally ended up in Leningrad which the next day would get back its original name of St Petersburg. There I visited the Efremov Institute, an accelerator magnet manufacturer, and that evening, by total coincidence, ran into my Stanford friend Jorge Fontana while attending the Tchaikovsky opera "Iolanda."

Following the failed coup against Gorbachev, the USSR was dissolved against his wishes, and he resigned. After leaving office, he launched his foundation, openly criticized Boris Yeltsin and later Vladimir Putin, and tried to promote a social democratic regime. Unfortunately, this system never materialized when the Russian economy was privatized, and the Oligarchs seized a large part of it.

Meanwhile, in 1990, Boris Yeltsin had been elected chair of the Russian Supreme Soviet and in 1991 president of the Russian Soviet Federative Republic (RSFR), and he officially dissolved the USSR in December that year. The RSFSR then became the Russian Federation, an independent state.

Between 1991 and the summer of 1993, the Russian Federation went through endless economic and political crises. The Russian GDP kept falling. Yeltsin and his Deputy, Aleksander Ruskoy took opposite sides in the constant conflict between the President and the Parliament, and the conflict finally became violent on October 3rd, 1993. By total coincidence, I arrived at the Moscow airport that afternoon to attend the annual meeting of the Joint Cooperative Committee on the Fundamental Properties of Matter (JCC-FPM). The person that met me at the airport informed me immediately that "there were emergency conditions in Moscow" and that I would be taken to the ITEP guest house via a circuitous route to avoid the violence in the city. Yeltsin had ordered troops to take over the White House (the Parliament), and rebels were assaulting the Ostankino TV station and other official buildings. When I arrived at the Guest House, I was rapidly escorted to my room where blinds had been drawn for safety, and I was instructed to stay put for the night, without food for dinner. There was a TV in the room, and I remembered from way back that if all you could see was Swan Lake, there was indeed trouble!

Early in the morning of October 4th, I was awoken with the good news that I would get some breakfast and that the situation in Moscow was calming down. My friend from Dubna at the time, Anatoly Krasnik, who feared I would starve, brought me a bag full of food all the way from Dubna. The JCC-FPM meeting took place more or less as usual on the 5th and 6th. With military help, after a few people were killed, Yeltsin put out the rebellion and the situation in Russia got back to "normal." I returned to the U.S. safely.

Following this, Yeltsin's leadership continued to go through many ups and downs, economic difficulties, wars in Dagestan and Chechnya, and other political crises. He was reelected in 1996 but forced to resign in 1999, at which point he turned the government over to Vladimir Putin. Yeltsin then assumed a low profile and died in 2007. Gorbachev outlived him but died on August 30th, 2022, at age 91, as I am writing these lines. Russia still has not recovered from its traumas, the latest being its miserable invasion of Ukraine.

Chapter 15

1994-1995

The year 1994 was marked by three major events at SLAC in which I got involved.

The first event took place early in the year with the official launching of the construction of the B-Factory. Since I had some previous experience with such affairs, Director Burt Richter and Project Leader Jonathan Dorfan asked me to organize the event. Surprisingly, after the demise of the SSC, the B-Factory project had been promptly approved in late 1993 with a budget of $177 Million. The purpose of the B-Factory was to study CP violation, i.e., the unbalance between matter and anti-matter in the B-Bbar sector. SLAC, LBNL and LLNL were going to collaborate in the construction of the machine. Meanwhile, a very similar machine called KEK-B was going to be constructed at KEK in Japan, a fact that would lead to a friendly and stimulating competition between SLAC and KEK.

The SLAC B-Factory, also to be known as PEP-II, was to be installed in the existing PEP-I tunnel. It would consist of a High Energy Ring (HER) storing electrons at about 9 GeV, and a Low Energy Ring (LER) storing positrons at 3.1 GeV, both receiving their particles from the same system as the SLC. Collisions would take place in one existing interaction region (IR2) where a large new detector called BaBar (for whimsical and obvious reasons) would be installed. Scientists from ten countries would participate in its design and construction.

The idea of colliding electrons and positrons of different energies had been proposed by LBNL's particle physicist Pier Oddone to cause the "boosted" center-of-mass of the collisions to move. As a result, if the decay times of the B and B bar, or anti B were different, the boost would turn the decay time into a flight length difference that could be observed along the detector. To make the description complete, it should be added that both the BaBar detector and the corresponding Belle detector at KEK would be set to the so-called Upsilon 4S resonance, just above the threshold for its decay into the two B mesons.

The celebration of the launch in the IR-2 Hall was attended by DOE Secretary Hazel O'Leary, Stanford Provost Condoleezza Rice, Senator Dianne Feinstein, Congresswoman Anna Eshoo, Congressman Norman Mineta, and some 300 lab managers and staff. Noticing that one of the female technicians had brought her baby-girl Rachel to the event, Hazel O'Leary threw away her prepared speech and decided to dedicate the B-Factory to Rachel and her generation. Also, as part of the event, a female crane operator ushered the first magnet onto the orbit of the ring. It turned out to be a colorful event, auguring well for the project that was completed four years later, on schedule and within budget.

The second event took place on June 23rd, 1994. Partially triggered by our close US-Japan collaboration, SLAC was honored by the visit of the Emperor and Empress of Japan. We were informed about the visit about a month ahead of time. which gave us ample time to organize it. I was again put in charge and had the great help of my excellent Administrative Assistant, Eleanor Mitchell. We made sure KEK Director Hirotaka Sugawara would attend the event and prepared a fancy bi-lingual brochure (Fig. 100) for the occasion. We met several times with the Imperial Chief of Protocol and decided that their Majesties would first be taken for a short tour of our three-kilometer klystron gallery, and then to the Collider Hall. To descend to the base of the SLD detector, the Emperor and Empress needed to take a three-story elevator in which the protocol allowed them to be accompanied by only one Japanese trusted official plus the operator. This process was carefully rehearsed with others ahead of time, yet had to be canceled at the last minute because the elevator operator panicked and irreversibly locked the elevator door before they could enter it. Cooler heads prevailed and we re-programmed the visit without a glitch. It gave more U.S. and Japanese scientists in attendance to line-up and shake hands with the Emperor and Empress, something that would be impossible in Japan.

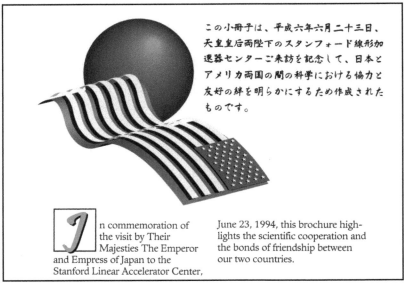

この小冊子は、平成六年六月二十三日、天皇皇后両陛下のスタンフォード線形加速器センターご来訪を記念して、日本とアメリカ両国の間の科学における協力と友好の絆を明らかにするため作成されたものです。

*7*n commemoration of the visit by Their Majesties The Emperor and Empress of Japan to the Stanford Linear Accelerator Center, June 23, 1994, this brochure highlights the scientific cooperation and the bonds of friendship between our two countries.

The Imperial couple is shown next page with Burt Richter in the Collider Hall (Fig. 101), and with the Emperor shaking hands with my long-time colleague Roger Miller, and the Empress with Martin Breidenbach, designer and builder of the SLD (Fig. 102).

The entire event was a great success.

The third event that culminated in 1994-1995 was more spread out in time. As I mentioned earlier, ever since the SLC

101

102

was being built, the world accelerator community was enticed by the possibility of building a linear collider that could reach a center-of-mass energy of at least 500 GeV. By 1992, there were six or seven candidate designs with possible chances of success. Burt Richter wrote a paper reviewing their various approaches and challenges. DESY in Hamburg proposed two separate models, one conventional S-band pair of copper linacs, similar to SLAC, and one pair of 1500 MHz superconducting niobium linacs called TESLA. BINP in Novosibirsk proposed a pair of 14 GHz high-gradient linacs. CERN proposed a pair of 30 GHz super-high gradient linacs, each supplied by a single drive beam (equivalent to one huge long klystron) called CLIC. SLAC and KEK proposed a pair of 11.4 GHz conventional copper linacs, and KEK added two similar conventional models, one at S-Band,

and one at 5.7 GHz. The problem was that their specifications and characteristics were all over the map.

Since I was reasonably familiar with all these approaches, I was asked to come up with a technical review to compare the statuses and prospects of all these machines for ICFA's assessment. For this purpose I engaged the help of representatives from every lab and spent the next two years producing the report. It was published in 1995 after several international meetings, discussions and occasional controversies. The report was well received but it concluded very clearly that much R&D was still needed and that no machine was ready for construction.

As we approached the end of the 20th century, what was the status of particle physics? The standard Model of Particle Physics looked almost complete, except that the Higgs particle had not been discovered. The SLC at SLAC and LEP at CERN were probably running out of energy to find it. Linear colliders looked promising but were not ready, and every one of them seemed too costly for any one country to build by itself. The SSC was dead, and the Large Hadron Collider in Europe looked like the earliest large enough machine to find the Higgs. The unbalance between matter and antimatter in the universe remained a mystery that was going to be studied by the two upcoming B-Factories at SLAC and KEK. The deficit of solar neutrinos observed on earth was still controversial and would not be fully understood until 2002. The nature of dark matter, six times more preponderant than visible matter according to observations by Vera Rubin and others, was not known. Dark energy that causes the universe's expansion to accelerate faster than Hubble's prediction, had been identified by two international teams but could not be explained either.

Chapter 16

Photon Physics with Synchrotron Radiation

Even though I personally never worked on photon physics research at SSRL, this book would be incomplete if I didn't devote a chapter to it. I mentioned earlier that synchrotron radiation had been discovered in 1973 at SPEAR and that it opened enormous research opportunities in material science, environmental science, biology and medicine, archaeology, and crystallography. In the 1980s, SPEAR physicists discontinued their electron-positron collision program, and solely dedicated it to synchrotron radiation from electrons. It got a local injector that made it independent of the linac. Sometime later SSRL came under direct SLAC management.

Fifty years later, SSRL is still going strong in parallel with SLAC's free electron laser or LCLS1. Under SLAC Director Chi Chang Kao, LCLS2, using a new superconducting linear accelerator, will soon come online as well.

Shown on the following page are illustrations of how the photon beams are extracted from all around the SPEAR storage ring and, for example, are directed onto a robotic crystal exchanger and sample target (Figs. 103, 104).

Two examples of important research projects are also shown following.

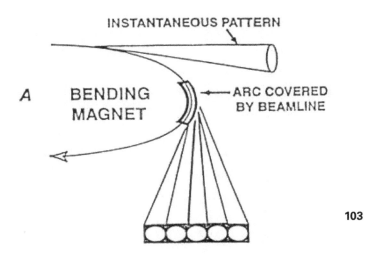

INSTANTANEOUS PATTERN

A   BENDING
     MAGNET

ARC COVERED
BY BEAMLINE

103

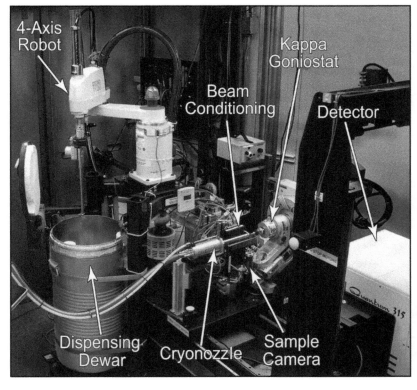

4-Axis Robot

Kappa Goniostat

Beam Conditioning

Detector

Dispensing Dewar

Cryonozzle

Sample Camera

104

The first one (Fig. 105 below) is the discovery at SSRL of the RNA Polymerase "machine" for which Roger Kornberg got the Nobel Prize in 2006.

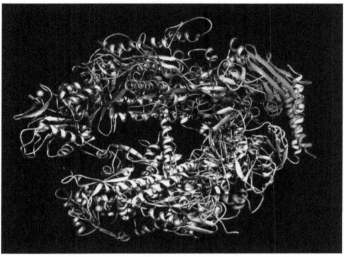

105

The second one is the discovery of the structure of the Anthrax Bacterium shown below with the lethal site illustrated on the lower right in light blue-green (Fig. 106).

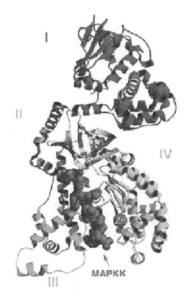

106

Chapter 17

1999-2008

Just before Burton Richter stepped down as director in 1999 and Jonathan Dorfan (Fig. 107) replaced him,, a controversy developed between the people in charge of the SLC/SLD collaboration, and the proponents of the new B-Factory The former thought that the SLC could continue to run for some years between B-Factory fills, but the latter were convinced that filling the two rings would be complicated enough to jeopardize a successful start-up of the new machine, even though the injection techniques were similar. In the end, the prospects of the SLC/SLD making another new discovery waned, and they agreed to stop the run, after just ten years. It was not an easy decision.

107

Jonathan had many very competent colleagues around him who had worked with him on the construction and the early commissioning of the B-Factory and the BaBar detector, but now he would also have to run the lab. At this point, I was still Deputy Director of the Technical Division, but he asked me if I could join him as his personal assistant. After giving it some thought, I agreed even though my family and I were going through difficult times. My wife Gilda had breast cancer, but she was bravely continuing to run her institute, traveling, going to the SF Opera with me, not letting non-family members know about her deteriorating condition. She fought a valiant battle, but modern medicine could not save her.

As I mentioned in Chapter 2, Gilda died prematurely at age 70 on January 5th, 2001.

About a couple of months later, Jonathan and I had a long talk and since our collaboration was going very well, he asked me to officially become his Deputy Director of SLAC, which I was very excited to accept. Around the same time, the International Linear Collider Technical Review Committee (ILC-TRC), was reconvened by the International Committee for Future Accelerators (ICFA). The idea promoted by David Burke was to reassess the current technical status of all electron-positron linear collider designs still active in the world. Jonathan asked me if I would lead that effort a second time, a very flattering offer I also accepted. This time, the assessment would involve a smaller number of machines: TESLA, JLC-X/NLC, JLC-C and CLIC. In some ways, these two jobs together would be very demanding, but also very rewarding.

I begin with the TRC job.

I worked with the second ILC-TRC for exactly two years. We formed six working groups with a total of about thirty members, plus a final reading group to check our report. As a group, we traveled all over the world to scrutinize every project. Nan Phinney and Tor Raubenheimer at SLAC were of particular help to me.

We organize our report by producing mega tables listing the specifications of the four proposals under review, including systems and subsystems. The common goal was to meet center-of-mass energies of 500 GeV, later expandable to higher levels. We analyzed respective states of machine readiness and reliability of operation. For each approach and technology, we tried to rank their prospects of current performance and remaining R&D needs. For example, TESLA was not yet consistently reaching its stated gradient goal of ~20 MV/meter. NLC/JLC could reach their gradient of 80 MV/meter in their structures but were still lacking reliable klystrons and pulse compression systems to drive them. CLIC used an interesting two-beam drive system but there was not yet an existence proof for their approach. All machines were going to need a considerable amount of electric power. Overall costs were not yet known with confidence. It was clear that the world science community could not afford to pursue two or three R&D approaches in parallel forever, and that it would be beneficial for everybody to make a choice.

The voluminous second report that was submitted to ICFA in February 2003 can be found on the Web. ICFA in turn formed a separate committee of thirteen "wise men" to make a choice between TESLA and JLC/NLC. Under the leadership of Barry Barish from Caltech (who subsequently shared the Nobel Prize for detecting gravitational waves at LIGO), they studied the two projects for almost a year and finally secluded themselves in So. Korea between August 11th to 13th, 2004, until they were able to come to a unanimous choice. The thirteen "wise men" are shown top of next page (Fig. 108).

Their decision, which they announced a couple of days later in Beijing: TESLA!

As readers can imagine, the choice was met with great disappointment at SLAC and KEK where we had been collaborating on the X-Band model for twenty years. It took a few weeks for our staffs to recover from the shock, but recover we did. Although the linear accelerators would now be made from superconducting niobium and not room temperature copper, some of the other systems like the damping rings and the final focus had some common features that kept members of both teams on board of the new International Linear Collider organization first called the GDE or Global Design Effort. By concentrating all its efforts on a single design and technology, the GDE was able to make more progress and gradually converge on a more robust machine.

In March 2006, Barry Barish asked me to join him at a conference in Bangalore, India to try to enlist that country into the ILC collaboration. Appropriately, my talk at the Indian Institute of Science was titled "The road to Bangalore."

This was a wonderful opportunity for me to see India where I had never been, and to visit my friends from Caltech, Rao and

Shyamala Valluri, who lived in Bangalore. Rao had been director of the National Aeronautics Laboratory for many years. I stayed with them for a week during the conference and afterwards was able to travel around with Rao for a few days to the magnificent thirteenth century temple of Somnathpur below (Fig. 109), Mysore, and the Kabini natural reserve below (Fig. 110). famous for its elephants, on one of which we took a long ride through the

109

110

forest. Bangalore itself was fascinating for its artistic and scientific cultural life, but also notorious, like most of India, for its over-population and endless traffic jams.

After Bangalore, I continued on to Agra to see the Taj Majal (Fig. 111), Jaipur where I witnessed an elephant procession (Fig.112), as well as a temple with an example of a typical traffic jam (Fig. 113), and New Dehli where I saw the Jantar Mantar observatory, built in 1724 to track the solar system (Fig. 114).

111

112

113

114

Coming back to the ILC, a little later, Japan decided to host the project and made considerable efforts to enlist the support of Japanese industry. However, MEXT, the Japanese funding ministry, also kept asking for substantial financial contributions from Europe, the U.S. and/or Asia for a 500 GeV project estimated to cost $5 Billion. Discussions dragged out until 2012 when the Higgs was found at the LHC with a mass of 125 GeV. This enabled the ILC design team to downsize its project to 250 GeV to start with, and to shorten the initial length of the site from 30 to 20 kilometers. Despite this, the international community, committed to other large projects, has not yet offered any funds to Japan. Some theorists firmly believe that an ILC is needed to do precision measurements on the Higgs but the prospect of CERN or China building 100 km circumference electron-positron circular colliders is muddying the waters. Hence, 18 years after the thirteen "wise men," made their choice, the ILC is still in limbo.

My tenure of working with Jonathan turned out to give me great intellectual satisfaction. I had been at SLAC since the beginning, knew most people at the lab, and felt I could be very helpful in this job. Jonathan had some excellent new ideas, and it was a pleasure to assist him.

SLAC had the deserved reputation of a "candu" place, and this at times caused people to be less than super-polite. In one of his first actions, Jonathan wrote a brief code of conduct he called "A respectful workplace" that was distributed to the entire staff. To improve internal and external communications, we hired the highly experienced Neil Calder from CERN who made an immediate difference in our public relations.

The B-Factory with BaBar was of course Jonathan's central scientific preoccupation but this didn't detract him from thinking ahead. Realizing the growing importance of astrophysics, he was able to convince the university to let us hire two new expert professors in the field, Roger Blandford from Caltech, and Steve Kahn from Columbia, to lead the effort. With these two leaders, Jonathan was able to get the science philanthropist Fred Kavli to donate the funds to SLAC and Stanford to build KIPAC, the Kavli Institute for Particle Astrophysics and Cosmology. This, with stars Blandford and Kahn, opened entirely new opportunities for the lab. The LSST or Large Synoptic Survey Telescope to operate in Chile at the Vera Rubin Observatory was one of the first major projects to be launched.

Jonathan also developed the concept of forming other joint institutes with Stanford, including PULSE and SIMES for photon physics research, and renovated the SPEAR ring to its third incarnation, SPEAR III. During his tenure, SLAC also led the development of the main instrument for NASA's Fermi Gamma-ray Space Telescope and secured the world's first X-ray free-electron laser, the Linac Coherent Light Source or LCLS from DOE. The Fermi-Spaced Telescope was successfully launched by NASA on June 11th, 2008, when Persis Drell was SLAC director. It has been very productive in the study of cosmic rays and is still operating, fourteen years later.

During all these years of innovation, did everything always go smoothly? Of course not. At the very beginning, we suffered from a complete power outage when a tree fell on a power line in Woodside. Then came 9/11. SLAC was not physically harmed but the DOE authorities got worried about the free access to our campus and tried to impose new restrictions with badging and special permits for foreign visitors. Fortunately, we were able to fully preserve our regime of academic freedom.

The most serious incident we had to deal with was an accident on October 11th, 2004, in which a contract employee suffered bad chest burns during the installation of a circuit breaker on a "hot" 480 KV piece of equipment. Even though the worker was not a SLAC employee and had made a mistake in judgment,

SLAC was blamed for a Typy1 safety infraction, and the accident led to a long and painful DOE investigation. All electrical workers were subjected to stringent safety training, and all 'hot" work was forbidden forever. The new rules slowed down a lot of maintenance work but were beneficial in the long run.

By 2005, Dorfan had been SLAC Director for six years and he decided that he would not stay in the position beyond 2007. To prepare the lab for younger management, he promoted his two Associate Directors, Persis Drell and Keith Hodgson, to Deputies, and I stepped down. I was then 75 and it made good sense. For the next three years, I kept several of my responsibilities on the electrical power procurement front, on the SLAC Colloquium Committee, on Faculty affairs and other scientific advisory jobs.

In 2007, Pief Panofsky died of a sudden heart attack, and we organized several events in his memory. After an unsuccessful outside search, Persis Drell became SLAC Director, and Jonathan went to work as an advisor to Stanford President John Hennessy. The B-Factory kept running successfully until 2008 when it was discontinued to make room for the LCLS. The CP violation measurements made independently by the B-Factory and KEK-B agreed perfectly with the theoretical predictions made in 1972 by Kobayashi and Maskawa, for which they got half the Nobel Physics Prize in 2008. By the way, the magnitude of this CP violation is not large enough to explain the existing dominance of matter over antimatter.

I want to end this chapter on another upbeat note. Indeed, if you look at the history of SLAC for the first thirty years, it was very exclusively a men's world. However, starting around the1990's, this situation began to change, and many outstanding women began to appear. I will list just a few here: Mimi Chang (Budgets), Helen Quinn (particle theorist), Vera Luth (experimentalist), JoAnn Hewett (particle theorist), Nan Phinney (linear collider specialist), Persis Drell (Director of SLAC, 2007-2012)), Risa Wechsler (astrophysicist), Natalia Toro (particle theorist), and Melinda Lee (head of Communications Department).

Finally in this vein, I want to mention our wonderful Congresswoman Anna Eshoo who was always most supportive of our laboratory. Her picture appears below (Fig. 115).

115

I will come back to Anna in later chapters.

I officially retired from SLAC on June 1st, 2008, exactly fifty years after I started to work on what was then called Project M at the W.W. Hansen Microwave Laboratory. You might think it would have been a traumatic day for me, but it was not. All that was really happening was that I now had the word "Emeritus" in front of "Professor" which sounded very sophisticated! Jonathan Dorfan organized a nice dinner party in my garden that was attended by about eighty people, Adele Panofsky, close colleagues, my children, and Mircea Fotino, born in Bucharest, Romania who had been my classmate at the Sorbonne in 1950 and lived in Boulder, Colorado. How about that for some continuity?

At SLAC I was given a nice office, Joe Ballam's old office, where I continued to carry out interesting activities for another twelve years until Covid-19 hit and all our meetings moved to Zoom.

My story would be incomplete if among my many good friends over the years, I didn't mention Anne Knight whom I met at a concert in Palo Alto in 2004. Anne and I had a close and entirely platonic friendship for sixteen years. She was a Harvard graduate in English and American literature, a voracious reader and a great conversationalist. She made a living by teaching English to foreign-born Palo Alto high school students. Anne introduced me to Henry James and his *Portrait of a Lady*," and we often went together to the Stanford Theater to watch old movies. Our favorites were Fred Astaire and Giger Rogers in their fabulous performances. Unfortunately, Anne died of lung cancer in 2020.

Chapter 18

Sixty years of electric power procurements at SLAC

Before I leave the subject of SLAC, I want to cover a subject of importance to the lab with which I became intimately familiar after Richard Neal stepped down in 1983: the interesting history of SLAC's procurements of electric power. At this point, this business which he had handled became part of my job. The history is worth recounting in that it closely mirrors other major developments in this field in California and the U.S. over the last one hundred years.

SLAC in 2022 is sixty years old. For the first 40 years and until January 1st, 2005, the lab enjoyed exceptionally low electric power rates. This was for two reasons. The first was due to Director Pief Panofsky's wise decision from the inception of the lab to secure a long-term contract with the Western Area Power Administration (WAPA) in Sacramento, now in Folsom. Most of WAPA's power came from dams along the Central Valley. Pief used to call it "socialist power" because it was essentially government power stemming from the Bureau of Reclamation created under FDR. Interestingly, the City of Palo Alto had a very similar deal with WAPA. The second reason we got an even better deal was because we had a large load which we could "volunteer" to turn off in the summer when the total WAPA load would exceed its capacity of about 1 Gigawatt. These were the infamous "brownouts" that exasperated many operators and physics users but saved us a bundle of money. For "old timers", the SLAC representatives who had to negotiate these unpopular brownouts were people like Larry Kral, Ev McKeen, Roger Erickson, Chris Foundoulis and Keith Reynolds.

For reference, a Gigawatt is a unit of power equal to 1000 Megawatts. When SLAC ran its program flat-out in the SLC and B-Factory days, our meter in the Main Control Room registered close to 60 Megawatts. When you are at home at night using your electric oven and running your dish washer, you may be using a few kilowatts. Note, however, that when you get your electric bill at the end of the month, you don't pay for power but for energy measured in kilowatt-hours. A kilowatt-hour is what you consume if you steadily use a kilowatt for an hour. In 1964, SLAC probably paid WAPA about 0.2 cents/kw-hour, and in 2004, about 2.5 cents!

The maximum SLAC allocation from WAPA was for a long time about 47 MW. Already in the PEP I and early SLC days, we often ran above 50 MW (and one time over 70MW), and the supplemental power was bought at a much higher rate from PG&E. The average cost, however, was still relatively low as compared to the market. Another feature which existed since the inception of SLAC was that WAPA and PG&E had a contractual agreement whereby they helped each other. This meant that when the WAPA dams were high, they would sell cheap power to PG&E, and vice versa, when the dams were low, PG&E would back-up (the expression in the industry was "firm-up") power to WAPA at basically the same low price.

As early as 1980, SLAC was assisted in these transactions by an able power consulting firm called Exeter Associates located in Maryland. In the early-1990's, DOE participated in the funding and construction of a third 500 KV inter-tie line coming down from Oregon. This enabled California (and WAPA) to procure less expensive power from the Northwest. The line ended in Tracy, near LLNL in Livermore and the opportunity was seized to connect it directly to LLNL. At this point, advised by Exeter, DOE decided that we would be in a much better bargaining position if all three DOE Northern California labs (SLAC, LBNL and LLNL) bought their power together as a single consortium. Upon its formation, the new consortium enjoyed wholesale status, aggregating the three labs' demand, and sharing combined WAPA allocations and a WAPA purchased power contract with a company in Portland called Pacificorp.

This favorable situation continued until the beginning of 2005. In the year 2000, however, with deregulation and the ensuing energy crisis, PG&E divested itself of most of its generating plants and became just a power distribution company. When it then went bankrupt, it warned WAPA that it would not extend the forty-year contract and would no longer "firm them up" after the beginning of 2005. With consumption up, WAPA also realized that it could no longer provide steady power as before. A favorable era was coming to an end.

To prepare the three labs for this new situation, DOE and our EXETER consultants went through long market studies. At one point, believe or not, it looked like Enron might give us a good deal! Luck had it that we didn't go for it, given Enron's total collapse soon thereafter. In late 2003, it was determined that DOE (with WAPA as its buyer and dispatcher) would have to go out to the real "capitalist" market for several parallel bids. This procedure, which took hard negotiations, culminated when the bids came in. To hedge our bets, like when you buy a mutual fund, over 100 MW of firm capacity for the three labs were contracted with two groups of companies, half in the Northwest, the other half in Northern California. This system of consecutive 25, 50 and 5MW contracts spaced over several years is still used today. The average wholesale rate, including the cost of transmission provided by WAPA or the California Independent System Operator (ISO), in 2022 is ~8 cents/kilowatt-hour. It is still a bargain compared to the 45 cents/kilowatt-hour retail price you pay at home to cook your dinner with electricity.

I should add that when I officially retired from SLAC in 2008, Roger Erickson ably took over this job. Because of climate change, things are changing. Power from the Northwest is no longer as competitive. PG&E is still not out of the woods, figuratively and practically. Roger also tells me that in keeping with the times, he is now looking with Exeter and our consortium into a possible 50 MW contract with a solar power plant in the Mohave Desert.

PART 3

Chapter 19

Teaching about world affairs at Stanford

Throughout this book, I have tried to mention the major political events taking place in the world since WW2. Unfortunately, the world situation had not improved significantly. Not unlike the League of Nations after WW1, the U.N. was not living up to its expectations. India's independence had blown up into a bloody partition with Pakistan with three subsequent wars. Just because the Soviet Union was boycotting the Security Council to support the PRC against Nationalist China in 1950, President Truman had been able to mobilize the U.N. against North Korea's invasion, but otherwise, the veto was paralyzing the U.N. under most circumstances. President Eisenhower obtained an armistice in Korea in 1953 but by 2022, no peace has yet been achieved between North and South. France's colonial wars in Indochina and Algeria had festered for years. The latter had brought down the Fourth Republic in 1958. Charles de Gaulle had ushered in the Fifth Republic at the time, but a popular rebellion and a referendum made him resign in 1969. Three wars had taken place between Israel and the Arabs. The Cuban Missile Crisis could have destroyed the world. The nuclear arm's race had caused world arsenals to reach the obscene level of almost 70,000 warheads. John F. Kennedy, his brother Robert, and Martin Luther King were assassinated. The U.S. war in Vietnam destroyed LBJ's presidency and was followed by

Richard Nixon who would eventually have to resign. The war left millions of Vietnamese and 58,000 Americans dead, and huge demonstrations at home, including at Stanford. Stanford students succeeded in forcing the university administration to ban all classified work on campus.

By 1970 I was working hard at the laboratory, but a sudden new opportunity arose for me. It came in the form of a university memorandum, sent to me by, once again, Professor Marvin Chodorow, the one that had steered me onto the job at Project M in 1958. The memo indicated that Stanford was creating a new series of weekly two-hour seminars that would be given for a full quarter to freshmen and sophomores. The assumption was that young faculty like me would choose subjects close to their specialty to give the students an opportunity to familiarize themselves with something outside their typical curricula. Faculty proposals were requested.

I could have picked a subject like particle accelerators but then I thought: "This is what I do all day long. How about something else, out of the box?' The students were unhappy about the war, so how about studying the causes of war. It seemed like a long shot, but I wrote a one-page proposal and sent it in. To my shock and surprise, even though this was far from my specialty, my proposal was accepted and approved. All I had to do was to deliver.

I spent all the free time I had (of which there wasn't much) in the next few months researching my topic. I read numerous relevant books on international relations, history, economics, anthropology, biology, psychology and so on, and prepared my course. The seminars, with only twelve students in attendance, were very interactive and my approach was well received. I gave a fair amount of homework, and the students wrote long final reports, I ended up teaching these seminars for more than ten years and improved them year-by-year. It was a tremendous leaning experience. As I will mention at the end of this book, it motivated me thirty years later to write about the human condition.

Chapter 20

U.S. Politics (1995-2016)

In all my years in the U.S. I was always an ardent Democrat, but it wasn't until the mid-1990's that I became politically active. I don't remember exactly what got me started, but meeting Anna Eshoo and the wonderful couple of Jim and Emy Thurber who always had Anna at their Los Altos holiday party was certainly an inspiration. I lived in the California 21st Assembly District (until it was redistricted twenty years later as the 24th) and began to attend their committee meetings regularly. Jan Epstein was my wonderful first chair.

My starting activity was to hold meetings at my house and garden in Atherton for our prominent Assemblymen. The first one was the wonderful environmentalist Byron Sher who also taught at the Stanford Law School. I still remember the cold winter day when he gave a fireside chat in front of our fireplace. Sher then became our Senator in Sacramento. The next Assemblyman was Ted Lempert who ran until he was term limited. Lempert was followed by Joe Simitian, a very gifted speaker who came to talk every spring before a large crowd in my garden, Joe went on to become California Senator, and eventually returned to our area to become Supervisor in Santa Clara County. Joe was always a keen observer of the political scene, including when he analyzed Trump's defeat of Hillary Clinton in 2016.

In all those years, I had been close friends and supporter of Ira Ruskin and his wife Cheryl of Redwood City. Ira had started as a member of the Redwood City City Council where he worked hard to improve the downtown area. In 2004 Ira ran for Assembly against Republican Steve Poizner, and defeated him against great financial odds. Ira also came to my garden crowd every spring to report on the state of Sacramento. Unfortunately, he died prematurely at age 70 of a brain tumor, just as he was planning to run for California Senate. The last 21st and 24th Assemblyman I actively supported was Rich Gordon. He was one of the first openly gay candidates to win. By an amazing coincidence, I ran into him and his partner in Buenos Aires when we were there on vacation!

Sometime around 1998, I got elected to the San Mateo County Democratic Central Committee, a step that gave me a more influential position in the party. One of the major bonuses was to enable me to attend the annual California Democratic State Convention with state-wide Democrats and candidates. In 2000 I strongly supported Al Gore for President and of course was very disappointed with the outcome of that election.

Then came the 9/11 disaster.

Within a few days, President George W. Bush together with the UK asked that the Taliban, in control of 80% of Afghanistan, arrest and deliver Osama bin Laden, the orchestrator of the 9/11 attack, who most probably was hiding there with other al-Qaeda fighters. When the Taliban refused, the U.S. promptly started bombing their strongholds and soon thereafter invaded the country. This move was very controversial but understandable since the U.N., which should have intervened, failed to do so. By December, the U.S. coalition was in control of Kabul and many other Afghan cities, but not the countryside. With hindsight, we know now that this war would go on for twenty years and that by 2021 the Taliban would unfortunately prevail.

To make things worse, a year or so later, the President convinced himself and his supporters that Iraq's Saddam Hussein was arming himself with weapons of mass destruction, WMDs to attack us. Since Saddam Hussein was already seen as a war criminal, it was easy to fall into that trap, and the U.S. made the huge mistake of invading Iraq on March 20th, 2003, on a false pretense. This second war strained our military forces even harder since we were already over-extended in Afghanistan, fighting the mujahideen, Al Qaeda and the Taliban.

The invasion coincided with the March 2003 California Democratic State Convention at which Howard Dean made a scathing attack on his fellow Democrats who had given Bush *carte blanche* for the attack. His speech was electrifying and in May, he announced his candidacy for 2004 President in Burlington, Vermont where he was a popular governor. As a result, Dean for America clubs were formed in many places, and some of us created one in San Mateo County. When Dean came in third in the Iowa primary, his campaign unfortunately collapsed, so we changed the name of our club to Democracy for America (also DFA). In the end, John Kerry won the nomination but lost the election to incumbent George W. Bush in November 2004. Through our SMC DFA club, I met many long-term friends and strong Democrats such as founder Rob Dickinson, Carole Dorshkind, Ashleigh Evans, Kacy McClure, Lorri Holzberg, Judy and Bill Orttung, Shirley Gaston, Marshall Dinowitz, Diana Reddy. Gail Sredanovic, Flavia Franco, Elsa Shafer, Suzy Raye and many others.

Even though Howard Dean did not become President, he left his mark with two important initiatives. One was that he was the first to successfully fund his campaign with thousands of small donations via the Internet. The second one, when he became chair of the DNC, was to insist that the Democratic Party support candidates in all fifty states, regardless of their chances to win. This strategy paid off in the 2006 and 2008 elections.

Indeed, in 2008 we had our rising star, Senator Barack Hussein Obama, running for President. Meeting, shaking hands with him and campaigning for him, starting in June 2008 immediately after my official retirement from SLAC, was an unforgettable experience. Our headquarters were a small crummy locale on El Camino Real in Palo Alto where we packed over fifty volunteers and computers to phonebank for Obama all over the country. We first had to help him beat Hillary Clinton, and then his Republican opponent, John McCain. When the latter chose Sarah Palin, governor of Alaska, as his running mate, it looked like a smart move, but she soon made so many mistakes, that it helped Obama and his VP, Joe Biden. Having two superb candidates and the terrific Chicago-based campaign organization brought us a resounding victory on November 4th, 2008.

Obama's first term could have been much easier, but he inherited the terrible subprime mortgage loan crisis, bank failures and subsequent Great Recession from President Bush. As a result, he had to spend his first two years in office trying to recover from it. This, plus his courageous move to enact the Affordable Care Act (or Obamacare), cost him Congressional votes and brought the advent of the disruptive Tea Party in 2010. This said, among many positive achievements, he officially ended the war in Iraq on December 15th, 2011.

When 2012 came along, I hadn't lost my enthusiasm for Obama, and I ran successfully for California delegate to the Charlotte Democratic National Convention. Voting there to select our next President turned out to be a very exciting experience for me. We then had to beat Mitt Romney, which was a bit of a cliff hanger, but worked out well in the end.

Obama's second term was punctuated by many successes of which the so-called JCPOA or Iran deal banning their nuclear weapons program, and the Paris Climate Change Agreement were two of the most memorable. But Obama underestimated the degree to which the U.S. was not a united county and that it did and still does have red and blue states.

At the Democratic National Convention of 2016, Hillary Clinton had won the nomination over her democratic rival, Bernie Sanders. She ran a reasonably good campaign but made several mistakes. The Russians had not wanted her to win and undermined her by hacking her website and turning over campaign information to Wikileaks and Trump. On November 8th, 2016, she won the popular vote over Donald Trump by 3 million votes but lost the election in the Electoral College by 227 to 304.

What happened to our democracy after Trump was elected is discussed in the next chapter.

Chapter 21

The threats to Democracy

If we want to analyze the problems of democracy in the U.S. and in the world, we must first clarify what democracy means and how it operates. The word comes from the Greek "demos" or "people", and "kratos" or "rule", i.e., rule of the people. But unlike the direct Athenian democracy where a limited fraction of the population (male landowners) could collectively propose, debate, and enact laws and make decisions, we in the U.S. and in many other countries live in a representative republic where we elect people to govern on our behalf. We should also take into account that in most democracies, the government must work within the framework of a market economy. Market economies can be efficient, but suffer from booms and busts, allow large income inequalities and poverty, and don't guarantee employment to everybody. The effectiveness of our electoral systems is based on the full participation of an honestly informed electorate, on our trust in our elected officials, and their respect for rules of democratic governance, in part enshrined in laws and/or a constitution. Ideally, these political conditions should exist in any country that wants to have a democratic system.

In actuality, many of these conditions are not met. Voter participation in the U.S. is rarely more than 65%. Voters often lack the information to make educated choices, they are misled by media driven by excessive money in politics, they are subjected to voter suppression, or they may be apathetic. When it comes to elected officials, you cannot expect them all to be angels, but you would want them to have some idealism, be intelligent, honest, and have a sense of organization and altruism. To get elected, they obviously must propose programs that have some popular appeal and are realizable, but they should not be demagogues.

How do demagogues operate? They work by pandering to the lowest instincts of voters and their fears. Fear of economic loss, fear of foreigners, fear of "dangerous" immigrants, fear of people who look different from them (brown or black), fear of Jews, fear of criminals against whom one must buy more guns, fear of climate change mitigation that will destroy the economy, fear of enemy countries, and so on.

Candidate and then President Donald Trump gained the admiration and loyalty of many voters by his apparent decisiveness to act. Unfortunately, he simultaneously played on all their above insecurities and appealed to their nationalism with his MAGA slogan. He tried to convince them that he knew how to protect their good jobs from moving abroad but did not really solve the problem. He attempted to gut Obama's Affordable Care Act, but never came up with an alternative program. He then completely mishandled the Covid-19 pandemic for fear that it would hurt the economy. He also cut corporate taxes by 14%, thereby creating a trillion-dollar deficit in the federal budget.

On the international front, Trump expressed his admiration for autocrats and strongmen like Vladimir Putin and Kim Jong Un, showed his contempt for NATO, and he withdrew the U.S. from the Paris Climate Agreement and from the international treaty with Iran banning their nuclear weapons program.

In the end, Trump retained the allegiance of many of his supporters, but he clearly lost the November 2020 presidential election to Joe Biden. Not willing to accept his defeat, he made the false assertion that the election had been stolen from him, and he incited the January 6th, 2021 insurrection to stay in power. Fortunately for the stability of the Republic, he failed.

In his first two years in the White House, Joe Biden's leadership has been rewarded with many accomplishments, despite his slim majorities in Congress. He gradually brought the pandemic under control with a rational policy of vaccinations, masks and social distancing. He restored our relations with our allies, rejoined the Paris Climate Agreement, decreased the federal budget deficit, and is doing what he can to contain Putin's murderous actions in Ukraine. In summer 2022 he passed the Inflation Reduction Act that decreases healthcare costs and infuses $369 billion over seven years to reduce the threat of global warming.

President Biden's constructive policies were rewarded in the November 2022 midterm elections where the Democrats retained their majority in the Senate and suffered only a minor loss in the House.

I hope that with the President's continued steady leadership, our democracy will emerge stronger and long-lasting.

Chapter 22

The existential threat of global warming

Currently, humanity is experiencing at least three existential threats: the potential use of nuclear weapons, pandemics, and climate changes due to global warming. All three pose serious but different challenges to us. In this chapter I want to review the causes of global warming, show which greenhouse gases, countries and human activities are most responsible for it, and what we must do globally to curb it.

How the greenhouse gases work

Global warming is caused by the following mechanism:

The radiation from the sun heats up our earth. This heat would normally be re-radiated into outer space by infrared radiation. However, our human activities annually emit about 50 billion tons or Gigatons of greenhouse gases of equivalent CO_2 (carbon dioxide). Of these, about 30-50% are absorbed by the oceans (thereby acidifying them and seriously affecting their entire ecology), and about a quarter are stored in trees and plants worldwide through the process of photosynthesis via the chlorophyll in the leaves. The remaining 17-20 Gtons accumulate each year in the atmosphere, and similarly to the glass covering a greenhouse, block the infrared radiation from escaping by reflecting it back to earth and raising its temperature. The total accumulation of these gases is about 3200 Gtons. Since the beginning of the industrial age, it has produced a temperature increase of about 1.2 degree Celsius with a total equivalent CO_2 gas density by volume of about 450 parts per million molecules in our atmosphere. The reason the word "equivalent" is used is because ~70% of the effect is due to CO_2. The remaining 30% is caused by CH_4 (methane in natural gas) which has a Green House Potential (GHP) ~28 times greater than CO_2, smaller amounts of N_2O (nitrous oxide) with a GHP of 280, as well as fluorine and other greenhouse molecules.

Future temperature increases

In 2015 when the Paris Agreement on Climate Change was signed by 195 countries, it was projected that if the world wanted to avoid the worst and most disruptive effects, the total temperature increase by 2050 would have to be limited to 1.5 degree Celsius. According to the Intergovernmental Panel on Climate Change (IPCC), we are NOT on track to meeting this goal. Already at the current 1.2-degree Celsius increase, the planet is witnessing very serious storms, floods, droughts, wildfires, and sea level rises. As examples, one third of Pakistan was flooded recently, and hurricanes are devastating Florida and Puerto Rico. Unless the countries that produce the most greenhouse gases make draconian cuts in the near future, which seems unlikely, we may well be headed towards a 2-degree Celsius rise or even higher by 2050, which could well be disastrous. Under these circumstances, ~30% of the high-altitude glaciers could melt, the Northern polar ice cap could disappear entirely, and the Siberian tundra permafrost may warm up and release all its methane, two entirely irreversible phenomena.

Major responsible countries

When we look at all the countries in the world, we see that a group of six are responsible for 26.7 Gtons, more than half the annual total release of greenhouse gases, as shown in Table 1 below:

Table 1

Countries in 2002	GTons	Tons/ Capita	% of Global Emissions	GDP in $Trillions
China	14	10	28%	18.3
United States	4	12	8%	23
European Union	3	7	6%	17
India	3	2.3	6%	3.5
Russia	1.7	1.1	3.4%	2.1
Japan	1.0	0.8	2.0%	4.5

Of these, the net contributions of probably China and certainly India will continue to increase for several years, and we don't know what effect the war in Ukraine will have on the other group of countries.

What was achieved at COP27 in November 2022?

As this chapter was being written, the twelve-day 27th Conference of the Parties has just ended in Sharm el Sheik, Egypt. Its major achievement has been that the wealthier industrialized countries have agreed to create a fund to pay the poorer developing nations for the losses and damages already incurred by them because of global warming. The details of the fund's size and who will benefit from it remain to be determined. Other than that, the U.S. and Japan made a commitment to Indonesia to help it wean itself financially from using its coal. Also, according to Michael Bloomberg, the participants seemed to gain a better understanding of how domestic private sectors and banks could be incentivized to invest in worldwide greenhouse gas reductions. Unfortunately, no other new firm commitments were made.

Bill Gates' excellent book and some of its consequences

One positive contribution that was made in 2020 was the comprehensive book published by Bill Gates on "How to avoid a climate disaster." The book doesn't have all the answers, but it creates a complete inventory of all the human sources of greenhouse gases and where technological innovations and investments are needed to curtail them. Table 2 below summarizes the world situation to which I have added the percentages in the U.S. for comparison.

Table 2

Human activities responsible for global warming (percentages)	World	U.S.
Producing electricity	27%	27%
Making things (steel, cement, plastics, etc,)	31%	22%
Growing things (plants, animals), land management	19%	10%
Transportation (cars, trucks, ships and planes)	16%	28%
Keeping warm and cool (heating, cooling buildings)	7%	12%

With this tabulation, Gates identified what he calls the Green Premium or excess percent cost incurred by a green technology that would avoid the release of greenhouse gases and figured out systematically what innovations are needed as early as possible to replace fossil fuels by the most efficient fully green sources. Gates addresses these two challenges in lengthy detail which I cannot possibly match here, but I am summarizing some of them below, adding some ideas of my own.

Technical innovations needed

1) **Electricity:** Many of the activities listed in Table 2 above include the use of electricity. If we consider that we will have to charge our fully electric car fleet and the upcoming increase in world population, the need for electricity may as much as triple (currently 5000 gigawatts of power). All of this will have to be clean green electricity. It must be generated by renewable solar or wind energy (which are both intermittent), some more hydroelectricity, possibly nuclear fission reactors (if they can ever be made safe, and their radioactive waste sequestered for thousands of years), and possibly nuclear fusion reactors. The very recent breakthrough at LLNL's National Fusion Ignition Facility is good news although it only yielded 1 kw-hour out for ½ kw-hour in. Barring any surprises, a commercial electric power station based on fusion is still ~30 years away. It will not create as much radioactive waste as fission reactors, but it will still not be free of it

The intermittency problem (daily and seasonal) of solar and wind may not be solved by storage batteries alone, but the energy may be stored in the future in hydrogen generated by electrolysis of water with excess renewable electricity. Safe hydrogen storage still requires considerable R&D.

2) **Manufacturing and construction:** The green premium of making steel and plastics may be brought down close to 1 by

replacing heat from greenhouse gases by electrical heat. On the other hand, the making of cement from limestone calcium and sand does not yet seem to have an affordable green alternative. A revolutionary invention is urgently needed for the construction of buildings, dams on rivers for hydroelectricity, and bridges, let alone dikes to protect us from sea-level rise).

3) **Agriculture:** With the projected world population growth, at least 50% more food will be needed. Plant growth can be increased with fertilizers containing phosphorous, potassium and nitrogen, but nitrogen has a problem because it turns into nitrous oxide which is a potent greenhouse gas. We will need to waste less food and produce better fertilizers to promote regenerative agriculture. Since aerobic composting works, could we mass produce artificial "manure" without methane, from plants? [Stay away from landfills!]

Cattle and pigs by belching and farting methane produce about 5% of world greenhouse gases. A recent discovery apparently reduces the methane belched by cows by feeding them small amounts of seaweed. This would be good news if implemented on a large scale. However, growing cattle and pigs is a very inefficient method of providing us with proteins and fats. The best way would be to drastically cut down on our red meat consumption.

As far as land management is concerned, the most important step we can take is to completely stop the destruction of rain forests (already cut back by 17% in Brazil). On the other hand, planting a billion new trees in the world as some have suggested is a losing proposition. We wouldn't even find the necessary water!

4) **Transportation:** There are currently about one billion cars in the world, most of them propelled by gasoline, or mostly by ethanol in Brazil. By ~2050 they will all have to be replaced by electric vehicles with inexpensive rechargeable batteries. The

same is true for small trucks and buses. As to large trucks, ships and planes, batteries are too heavy for them, and we will have to produce biofuels or electro fuels to propel them. Sugar cane and switchgrass are good sources but much more R&D is needed in this area.

5)**Buildings:** Buildings will have to be much better insulated, and heated and cooled entirely by electricity. The efficiency of current air conditioners can easily be doubled, but the use of gas for air conditioners and water heaters can best be replaced by heat pumps.

In all these areas, we must increase conservation and discourage wasteful consumption.

Are there any other methods available to 1) decrease greenhouse gases in the atmosphere, or 2) decrease the sunlight heating the earth? Yes, but they are long shots. The first category includes Carbon Capture and Storage (CCS) at the point of production like a cement factory, but where to store the gas securely is not obvious. Another possibility is to directly capture the gas from the atmosphere with an absorbing surface. This process works but is not very efficient. The second category includes reducing the sunlight heating the earth by releasing billions of light-reflecting sulfur micro pellets into the upper atmosphere.

However, this form of geoengineering may take at least ten years to develop and a fleet of high-altitude airplanes to spread around the planet, and it may cause irreversible collateral damage. Another less invasive technique would be to make clouds brighter and more light-reflective by seeding them with salt.

Economic obstacles and incentives

We have just seen that to solve our global warming problem, we will need many innovations. If all these innovations had a green premium of less than 1, i.e., if the green technology were less costly than the current non-green one, we could count on the market economy to adopt it naturally within a short transition period. Unfortunately, this is not the case.

When George H. W. Bush became President in 1988, like many Republicans at the time, he was ideologically inclined to make the fight against global warming an important part of his agenda. After all, President Richard Nixon had already created the E.P.A. (Environmental Protection Agency) in 1970. Unfortunately, Bush's chief-of-staff John Sununu talked him out of it: "it's going to hurt the economy and your popularity." Bush acquiesced and most Republican politicians since then have followed suit. Fundamentally, it's possible that many of them are not climate deniers in principle but worry that fighting global warming affects the economy negatively and antagonizes the oil, gas and other businesses that support them. They don't fully appreciate that a green economy can result in enormous new business opportunities and jobs. Maybe, some of them will change their minds in the future for this reason and for the good of the planet.

Who pays to curb global warming?

Global warming affects the entire world but is caused predominantly by the wealthiest industrial countries. We don't know exactly what it will cost to fix it, but we know that the people who will suffer the most if it isn't curbed are the poorest. We do know also that if the money is NOT spent now by the richer countries, the cost of sustaining the planet later will be much higher for all. The current annual GDP of the world is 96 trillion dollars. As seen in Table 1, the U.S., the European Union, Japan and Russia add up to half of this. Except for Russia in the current atmosphere, you might think that these rich countries together could easily spend $200 billion per year (less than ½%) on this problem to save the entire world community. To put this number in perspective, consider that with its 2022 Inflation

Reduction Act, the Biden Administration has dedicated $369 billion to deal with the problem domestically over the next seven years. That is $50 billion per year, a large sum but nothing in comparison with our defense budget of $858 billion this year!

In the last three chapters of his book, Bill Gates also makes many constructive economic suggestions on how governments at all levels, private sectors, universities, foundations (like his) and we as individuals can help this cause. Here are a few examples.

Governments can act to slow down population growth to decrease overall demand. They must greatly increase R&D to speed up the necessary innovations via their national laboratories, universities or other research institutions. Gates seems to favor raising carbon taxes, fees, or cap-and-trade systems, but Bill McKibben has given convincing arguments that it is far too late now for these measures to have a decisive effect: even a large tax of $100 per ton of carbon would do nothing. Besides, economist Paul Krugman argues convincingly that government subsidies have a better chance of overcoming political opposition. Then, once the proper innovations become available, the governments must help them make it to the market at large, "beyond the so-called valley of death." The private sector can then feel safe investing in these innovations just as it is building solar and wind plants, because they are profitable.

State and local governments can and often do (but not always) adopt positive policies like California with its automobile fuel efficiency standards. In San Mateo County where I live, we have the Peninsula Clean Energy coalition which only delivers renewable electricity and the very climate-proactive State Senator Josh Becker. Stanford University with the Precourt Institute, the Woods Institute for the Environment and the new Doerr School for Sustainability is also making important R&D investments in the field.

On the other hand, the California Public Utility Commission

(CPUC) took a highly regressive step on December 15th, 2022, against future solar rooftop owners in the state. As a result of fierce lobbying by the private utilities like PG&E, the CPUC changed the rules by which any new owners will be compensated from now on. Under previous (so-called NEM2) rules, California utilities paid for a private solar kilowatt-hour delivered to the grid about the same (30 cents) as they charged for a conventional kilowatt-hour purchased from them after sundown. In contrast, under the new (NEM3) rules, they will pay only 25% (~8 cents) for a solar-produced kilowatt-hour after April 15th, 2023. Although the 1.5 million current owners (like me) will be grandfathered under the old rules, this will discourage future potential homeowners from buying solar panels unless they are wealthy enough to pair them up with storage batteries that are still far too costly (up to $20 thousand for a 13-kWh battery). Very poor decision for sunny California!

Finally, we as individual consumers have other options. We can buy electric cars, which will be helpful as long as we recharge their batteries with clean green electricity and we can install heat pumps outside our houses to get rid of natural gas. We can switch from cow to soy or oat milk (just as good), and to paraphrase Nancy Reagan, we can "just say no to red meat!" The cattle ranchers and butchers will not love us for this and will fight these steps tooth and nail, but they will have to adapt. Cows and sheep may be grown just for leather and wool. Free-range poultry, fish (even farmed) and other seafood may still be used for human consumption, helping us lower our cholesterol and heart disease. Third-world countries can make important contributions in these areas.

Never underestimate what individuals can do. One example that stands out is former Professor Art Rosenfeld at UC Berkeley and LBNL who completely revolutionized energy conservation standards, first in California and then everywhere else. He developed new heat-trapping windows, new light bulbs, caused industry to double the efficiency of refrigerators, and computer-modeled the improvement of buildings for temperature control. Art ended up becoming California Energy Commissioner and working for the Clinton Administration, where he probably inspired VP Al Gore with his ideas. Art's innovations spread all over the world.

Some conclusions

The famous economist John Maynard Keynes pointed out that *demand* is what pushes the economy into action. And fear is a strong promoter of demand. When Covid-19 hit humanity as an existential threat, government and the private sector didn't waste much time to work together to produce vaccines, even though many people were vaccine deniers. The danger of the Maldives, Bangladesh, Madagascar, Florida and coastal cities like New York and San Francisco being under water and creating millions of refugees is just as scary as the pandemic and should trigger even greater demand.

The world spends close to 2 trillion dollars per year for defense, including horrible nuclear weapons, with very little popular objections but argues ad nauseam over a small fraction of this sum to fight global warming.

Here is one more suggestion. As a scientist who worked all his life with particle physicists, I am keenly aware of the prestige and excitement created annually by the Nobel Prize. Why not ask one or two wealthy people like Bill Gates and Michael Bloomberg to create a billion-dollar fund together to establish a Prize to save our planet?

Let us act collectively now before it is too late. Greta Thunberg and our grandchildren will be here in 2050 and they will never forgive us if we don't.

Chapter 23

The secret of The Human Condition

At some point in 2015, I decided that I wanted to organize and memorialize various ideas and thoughts that had puzzled me during my career at Stanford. Eventually, I converged on a project to write a book on *The Human Condition: Reality, Science and History*. The project led me to investigate many diverse topics related to philosophy, evolution, perception, free will, language, religion, economics, climate change, domestic and international political systems, wars and arms control, and possible reform of the U.N. It included the contributions of many of my heroes and heroines, A cover of the book is shown below (Fig. 116).

116

The book was first published by Mascot Books on August 6th, 2019 and reprinted in 2022 with a few minor corrections and updates.

I started the book by pointing out that evolution has brought our species to a point where we are capable of amazing achievements and dismal failures.

We can feel and express love and empathy, we know how to sacrifice and cooperate. We can plan for the future. We create literature and art, compose and play beautiful music, we can land on the moon, and develop cures for diseases and vaccines for pandemics. We successfully develop scientific knowledge as described throughout this book.

But side-by-side with these constructive behaviors and activities, we can be very destructive, we are able to hate, make war, kill millions of people, we don't know how to govern ourselves, and fall for demagogues, we allow famines and extreme income inequalities, religious intolerance and extremism, gender and racial discrimination, thirteen thousand nuclear warheads and global warming that both pose existential threats to our survival.

I summarized this dichotomy by asserting that our species **Homo is not yet Sapiens,** and still has much work to do to deserve this name. Throughout the book, I came up with some suggestions that might help us reach that status.

Of course, I didn't mean to say that there are no wise men and women in this world. As a matter of fact, if you read this book to the end of the Appendices, you will see that I have mentioned many wise human beings, physicists like Pief Panofsky, a President like Barack Obama, a Congresswoman like Anna Eshoo, an anchorwoman like Judy Woodruff, friends in politics like Emy Thurber and Ashleigh Evans, a taxi driver like Hector of Oaxaca, and so on. Their example has certainly influenced me, but how do we convert 8 billion people? How do we motivate then? The fear of God's punishment is not the right way.

Well, at the end of my "Human Condition", I let the readers in on a secret: "If we were wiser, we would certainly be happier." Happiness is something every human being wants, so if they realized that happiness is a reward for behaving wisely, that might be the carrot to offer as enticement. People like Hitler had power for a while but for sure they were never happy. Donald Trump may enjoy money and power, but he is not a happy man. And so on…

So let your friends and children in on the secret. Explain to them that they will not be happy all the time, that they may get sick or suffer from an accident, a loss, a divorce or a mishap, but that if they behave wisely, they'll be more likely to cope and recover.

And if they like classical music, just tell them when they feel unhappy, to watch and listen to Hélène Grimaud play Beethoven's fourth piano concerto with the Paris Orchestra under the direction of Christoph Eschenbach. She is sublime.

APPENDICES

Appendix 1

Excerpts from my book review of *Panofsky on Physics, Politics, and Peace: Pief Remembers*
(Updated in 2022)

Introduction: Genesis of the Book

When Springer publishers approached Wolfgang K. H. Panofsky (hereafter called "Pief" as he was affectionately known to almost everybody) in February 2006 to ask him to write his autobiography, he was almost 87 years old. This was a very fortunate initiative because Pief had always been too modest and reluctant to write such an autobiography, and without an invitation from a respected science publisher, the review of this wonderful book here would not exist. The broad community of scientists, politicians and friends who came into contact with this amazing man would have been deprived of this treasure of memories of Pief's life experiences and observations. What is also extraordinary about the book is that its contents were almost entirely dictated from memory to his assistant, Ms. Ellie Lwin, in part from a hospital bed when Pief was treated for congestive heart and lung failure in late 2006. Putting mind over matter however, as he had many times before, Pief subsequently returned to his office at SLAC on a regular basis. Even on the last day of his life, September 24, 2007, he came in and held several meetings with administrative and scientific colleagues before driving himself home. Had Pief not agreed to write this book, somebody else would probably have been invited to do so, but nobody could have done such a beautiful and comprehensive job. We must also thank Ms. Jean M. Deken and her archives staff at SLAC for their great editorial assistance in helping Pief with gathering missing dates and facts relevant to the material.

Nature and Nurture: Pief's Early Life

When one looks at the life and accomplishments of an individual, it is always interesting to consider how they were affected by both nature and nurture. In Pief's case, there is no doubt that both played equal roles. Pief had a prodigious intelligence and memory and he came from an illustrious family. As he mentions in the first chapter of the book, he was born in Berlin on April 24, 1919, the second offspring of Erwin and Dorothea Panofsky who met at an art history seminar. Erwin Panofsky was a world renown art historian, Pief's maternal grandfather, Albert Mosse, was a famous jurist assigned to assist the Japanese government to draft a constitution during the Meiji Restoration, his aunt, Martha Mosse, was the first woman to serve as police commissioner of the city of Berlin, and his uncle, Rudolf Mosse, was the publisher of the Berliner Tageblatt.

One year after Pief's birth, Erwin Panofsky accepted a faculty position at the University of Hamburg where the family lived from 1920 to 1934. Pief's elder brother of two years, Hans, was equally bright and both spontaneously developed an early interest in science and technology, unlike their parents who jokingly called them "Klempners" (plumbers) as they were growing up. When the reviewer, as a graduate student, first heard of Pief at Stanford in 1954, there was this legend that one of the brothers was called the "smart Panofsky" and the other "the dumb

Panofsky" (both were supposed to have inordinately high IQs differing by only two digits). I never did know which Panofsky was which, and asked Pief a few months before his death if he could clarify the issue, to which he answered: "No comment".

117

Pief at age about 4 years playing chess with his cousin Ruth Mosse, while brother Hans looks on. (Credit: Panofsky Family Collection.)

Flashing back to nurture, soon after the Nazis came to power in 1933, most professional German Jews like Erwin Panofsky lost their jobs and other civil rights, and Pief's father had to leave Germany, even though he lived in one of the more liberal cities in the country. He eventually secured a double appointment at New York University as well as at Princeton, where the family of four settled in 1934. One might guess that without the Nazis, Pief would have become a successful and well-known scientist in Europe anyway, but these developments and WWII certainly propelled Pief's life into the much broader intellectual and political orbit that is the subject of this book.

This Review

Pief points out modestly in the Preface that his book is an "unsystematic account" of his life and work. This is only true to the extent that he does not cover in detail all that other biographers might include, namely family life and children, all his numerous friends and acquaintances, and his vast accomplishments and professional contacts. The book, however, benefits from describing all his major activities while not being too long, so that one does not get lost in the trees of the forest. Pief's "essence" is all there, and the fact that he sometimes departs from chronological order by compartmentalizing his accounts by topics in separate chapters, makes the book that much more readable. The three major topics covered in the book are his own scientific experience, science advising and international science, and arms control. These will be reviewed here in sequence, with major emphasis on the first topic.

High School in Hamburg, University at Princeton and Caltech

Pief started his high school education in Hamburg at the Johanneum Gymnasium with essentially no science training. When he arrived in Princeton at age 15, his parents were able to enroll him and his brother directly into the university, temporarily on probation. As the reader may guess, probation was soon lifted since they were both excellent students. To their classmates who considered them somewhat as "oddballs", they were Piefke and Paffke (from two German cartoons), and the name, "Pief" for short, stuck with him for the rest of his life. The book contains many details about his Princeton education, the most relevant perhaps to this review being his senior thesis on radiation measurements with a high-pressure ionization chamber which used isotopes produced at the small Princeton cyclotron. Familiarity with this accelerator perhaps had some influence on Pief's future career. Other experiences at Princeton which enabled Pief to learn about American society are well worth reading in the book. His father befriended Einstein at the Institute of Advanced Studies and since neither one could drive, Pief became their occasional chauffeur at age 16! One time, a cop stopped him with Einstein in the passenger seat. When Pief asked the cop if he had done something wrong, the cop answered: "No, nothing wrong, I just wanted to take a close look at your passenger!"

After graduating from Princeton in 1938, Pief received a personal letter from Robert A. Millikan to join Caltech as a graduate student, with a teaching assistantship. He accepted this offer, which turned out to be a seminal decision. Pief eventually went to do his PhD thesis under Prof. Jesse DuMond, performing a precision measurement of the ratio of Planck's constant to the charge of the electron, and also getting acquainted with the boss' eldest daughter, Adele. Pearl Harbor happened in the middle of this, and by 1942, Pief got his degree, was teaching U.S.

118

Pief and future wife Adele on the steps of the Athenaeum at Caltech on the day of his Ph.D. ceremony, 1942. (Credit: Panofsky Family Collection.)

generals classes in electromagnetic theory, started defense work on an acoustic device called a Firing Error Indicator (FEI), got his U.S. citizenship, and married Adele. What a year!

Pief and the Bomb

Two years later, Pief's work on the FEI which measured shockwaves from supersonic bullets attracted the attention of Luis Alvarez and J. Robert Oppenheimer who were interested in measuring the yield of nuclear detonations for the Manhattan Project. As a result, Pief was invited to work at Los Alamos as a consultant, and a year later a shock wave detection device he developed was supposed to be tested by him with others on July 16th, 1945 from a B-29 airplane over the Trinity plutonium bomb test in Nevada. Although the test did not take place as planned for last minute reasons of weather and safety, similar gauges were later used over Hiroshima and Nagasaki. Pief discusses these events in some detail. It is clear that his awareness of the enormity and gravity of their long-term consequences shaped many of his actions for the rest of his life.

Accelerators and Physics at UCRL

After WWII ended, Pief agreed to join Alvarez at the University of California Radiation Lab (UCRL) directed by E. O. Lawrence, to work on proton linear accelerators, even though at that time he had no experience in nuclear physics or accelerator design. Ironically, his first two days at UCRL were spent inside the 184-inch cyclotron magnet as people noticed upon his arrival that he was the only person short enough to stand inside to make magnetic measurements. He then went on to lead the group which successfully designed and built the 32 MeV, 40-ft drift-tube proton linac. Several breakthroughs such as beam phase stability discovered by McMillan and Vecksler, cavity mode-mixing remediation due to the variable length of the drift tubes (calculated by Pief) and multipacting avoidance, led to the successful completion of this enterprise. However, while the linac was used to do physics, it did not lead to the construction of higher energy proton linacs at the time because of the parallel success of the less costly proton synchrotron. Note that while all these machines were already auguring the era of "big science", the culture of the time was much less specialized than today in that the physicists who built these machines considered them to be the necessary initial stages of their particle physics experiments and were the same people who then went on to perform these experiments. Pief was very much a beneficiary of this culture, and later it made him an example of somebody who was equally knowledgeable about both fields and could lead both enterprises from personal knowledge.

At the time Pief began to participate in particle physics experiments, it is noteworthy that he also accepted a heavy teaching load at UC Berkeley and decided to write his textbook on "Classical Electricity and Magnetism" with Melba Phillips. While he started to study proton-proton scattering at 32 MeV with the linac, his most exciting experiments turned out to involve pi mesons from the 184-inch cyclotron. From pi minus mesons impinging on protons and deuterons at rest, Pief and graduate students were able to identify the existence of the pi zero meson and measure the masses of the pi minus and pi zero (as well as their mass difference) to about 1% accuracy by looking at the gamma rays emerging from the reactions (and their decays into electron-positron pairs). From these measurements, it was also inferred that the pions are pseudoscalar particles, namely that they have spin zero and negative intrinsic parity. Pief often indicated that this work may have been his best. Later on, using McMillan's synchrotron, the measurements were confirmed by experiments done by him in collaboration with Jack Steinberger.

Events leading up to the Loyalty Oath

By late 1949, we get to perhaps the most pivotal point in Pief's life. Following the first Soviet nuclear test on August 29 and Truman's decision to proceed with the hydrogen bomb, Lawrence and Alvarez decided that they wanted UCRL to contribute to the project and find ways to produce tritium or breed plutonium with large quantities of neutrons. After considering various methods, they converged on a proton and deuterium linear accelerator modeled after the earlier 32-MeV machine but at the much lower frequency of 12 MHz which had a diameter of 60 ft. Code-named the Materials Test Accelerator (MTA), its first stage (87 ft. long) was eventually built at an abandoned naval air station near Livermore (which later became LLNL). Somewhat reluctantly, because he was already having strong second thoughts about further nuclear weapons, Pief worked on the microwave cavities for the project. But then, other political events caught up with him at UCRL. These are too lengthy to recount here but eventually led to the Loyalty Oath whereby the university, in Pief's words, would require its employees to "affirm their lack of Communist contamination". Pief signed the oath but became very upset when others who had refused to sign it were threatened with dismissal, and as a result, he decided to resign from the lab. Alvarez tried to dissuade him but Leonard Schiff and Felix Bloch at Stanford got word of his resignation and successfully enticed him to come to Stanford. Would SLAC be here if all this hadn't happened? We will never know. What we do learn from this incident and many other subsequent ones is that Pief never seemed to hold any grudges. Despite his fundamental disagreement with Alvarez, he maintained his friendship with him after he left Berkeley.

Stanford, the Microwave Lab and HEPL

When Pief and his family of six arrived at Stanford in early July of 1951, they moved into a big 1907 house in Los Altos where they lived forever after. The university and in particular the physics and electronics departments at the time were going through an unprecedented period of expansion. Pief joined both the Physics Department and the Microwave Laboratory. At the latter, he immediately got involved with the MARK III linear accelerator whose conception and early construction had started under the remarkable leadership of physicist William W. Hansen, with help from the inventors of the klystron, Russell and Sigurd Varian. Hansen died prematurely of lung disease in May 1949, but the construction of the MARK III continued successfully under the leadership of Ed Ginzton with a gifted team consisting of Marvin Chodorow, R. L. Kyhl, Richard Post, Richard Neal and many others. Actually, when Pief arrived, there were a number of problems with the traveling-wave accelerator sections (which arced at high gradient) and with the reliability of the klystrons and modulators. The arcing problem forced the designers to add more sections, all running at more modest gradients, thereby lengthening the entire accelerator to the point where there was no room left at the end of the building for experiments. Robert Hofstadter, who had come from Princeton in 1950, had to begin his physics research program with a spectrometer located at the halfway point of the accelerator. This problem led to Pief's first challenge: extend the building so that it could accommodate an appropriate beam switchyard and end-station. The job required working with university architects, getting financial support from Ginzton, having the experimental area designed, etc., which taxed all his physics and administrative skills. A large mound of earth excavated for the job was piled up at the end of the new extension and served as a beam stopper. When I arrived at Stanford, it was known as

Mount Panofsky! Emerging from the beam switchyard, there were two separate beam lines: one for Hofstadter's electron scattering experiments (for which he was awarded the Nobel Prize in 1961), and a second one for general use. This arrangement much later led to similar designs, albeit much larger, for SLAC.

Pief relates in considerable detail all his early experiences with his colleagues, the Office of Naval Research (ONR) which funded most of the work, the Physics Department where he soon carried a heavy teaching load, and his interactions with Ed Ginzton. Eventually, Pief and Ed decided to split their labor and responsibilities: the laboratory was divided into two parts, the High Energy Physics Laboratory (HEPL) of which Pief became director, and the Microwave Laboratory for microwave tube research, headed by Ginzton. Both together were named the W.W. Hansen Laboratories.

By then, Pief had a large family with five children, was teaching, carrying out and directing research, traveling a lot and getting increasingly involved in arms control work on a national scale. Pief himself wonders (and the reader does too) how he was able to keep so many activities going simultaneously. The main explanations one can find are that he worked extremely hard, that he was an extraordinary planner, and that he was also amazingly quick.

The "general use" second beam line was exploited mostly by Pief, his colleague from Berkeley, Robert Mozley (and Mozley's student Richard Taylor), and eventually a sequence of 13 other graduate students. A number of experiments were devoted to pions produced directly by electrons in contrast to those using gamma rays at Berkeley. Various people like Karl Brown, George Masek, Daryl Reagan, Peter Phillips and Lou Hand came to work under Pief's supervision. With Karl Brown they designed a double-focusing spectrometer, with George Masek they electromagnetically produced muon pairs, and with Peter Phillips they designed the first single-cavity radiofrequency deflector. This experiment was also connected with what is known as the Panofsky-Wenzel theorem which specifies the properties of electromagnetic modes capable of deflecting charged particles transversely (interestingly, Pief forgot to mention this theorem in his book!). By 1956, he was joined at HEPL by Research Associate Burton Richter who, sensing the energy limitations of the MARK III, together with Princeton's Gerard O'Neill and Carl Barber, designed and then built the pioneering electron-electron storage ring collider. This work was eventually superseded by Richter's and others' much more successful electron-positron colliders.

The Rise of SLAC

The success of the MARK III electron accelerator, both as a machine eventually reaching over 1 GeV in energy and as a rich source of particle physics research, inevitably led to the "next step" question. Speculations were started by Robert Hofstadter and were followed by numerous conversations involving him, Pief, Ginzton, Leonard Schiff, Richard Neal and others. A first report exploring the possibilities of a machine much larger than the MARK III was presented at the 1956 CERN Symposium on High Energy Accelerators by Pief and Neal. Meanwhile, a series of meetings was organized to come up with a proposal, the first of which was held in the evening of April 10, 1956 at Pief's home. (Note in passing that quite by coincidence, April 10, 2008 was chosen as the date for an international symposium at Stanford to celebrate Pief's life).

The formal "Proposal for a Two-Mile Electron Accelerator" which was written with the help of young English major Bill Kirk, came out in April, 1957. It was a relatively short report of 64 pages plus appendices, which was submitted simultaneously to the Office of Naval Research (ONR), the Atomic Energy Commission (AEC) and the National Science Foundation (NSF). In retrospect, Pief considered the technical part of the proposal a little naïve but thought that the cost estimate was realistic. After submission of the proposal for what was originally called Project M for "Multi-BeV" or "Monster", there followed a long protracted period of ups and downs. Several controversies arose in the university, in the scientific community, and in the AEC (which was eventually chosen to be the funding agency), in the Executive branch of the government and in Congress. The description of these anxiety-producing but fascinating (in retrospect) events occupies over ten pages in the book and is much too long to recount here.

In the end, SLAC was created as a separate entity from the Stanford Physics Department (in Pief's words "academically joint, administratively separate from the university") and as a national facility. Upon the death of the two Varian brothers, Ed Ginzton who had directed the Project M research phase, resigned from Stanford to assume the leadership of Varian Associates, leaving Pief as director of SLAC. Pief used all his persuasive powers to overcome a number of the Joint Committee on Atomic Energy's positions, such as the AEC wanting to run the A&E firm, not wanting to let Stanford's H&R policies prevail over the government's, and insisting on allowing classified work on the site. Pief won out on all these points. President Eisenhower endorsed the project in 1959 and the Democratic Congress finally approved its construction on September 15, 1961 with a budget of $114M. The contract and a separate land lease of the Sand Hill site for 50 years were signed in April 1962, and ground breaking started in July 1962.

Building SLAC

Of all his accomplishments, building SLAC was probably Pief's "finest hour". Again, the description of this period is much too long to recount here in detail, but a few salient topics and incidents should be mentioned.

What made Pief such an effective director and project leader were his total commitment, his incredible intellect, his ability to delegate, his technical insights to jump in when a difficult scientific problem arose, the trust he created with his staff through his willingness to listen and his humility. Of course, Pief does not advertise these qualities in the book, but the reader may discern them intuitively.

The line organization Pief chose for the lab was nimble and efficient and it survived for almost forty years. People like his business manager Fred Pindar, his head of administrative services Robert Moulton, his first deputy director Matt Sands, and research division associate director Joe Ballam are often mentioned for their contributions. One of the people Pief held in enormous regard was Richard (Dick) Neal, head of the technical division, who was in charge of the construction of the entire accelerator and all its subsystems.

Two specific areas where Pief made personal technical contributions to the accelerator are noteworthy. One was his idea to enable the linac operators to instantly detect where the beam was poorly steered in the 3 km accelerator, producing radiation along the way. For this he proposed an argon-filled 3 km long coax cable along the machine which would get ionized and break down at the location where the radiation was produced. The breakdown pulse profile was constantly displayed on a scope in the control room. The device functioned very well and was called PLIC, for "Panofsky's Long Ion Chamber". Pief's second personal contribution took place immediately after the first 15 GeV beam was steered down the accelerator in April and May 1966 and exhibited a detrimental behavior called "beam break-up" which has already been described earlier in this book.

The construction of the accelerator was completed in the summer of 1966 within schedule and within budget. The official dedication took place the next year in September 1967.

119

*SLAC Dedication, September 1967. From left to right, Glenn Sea-
borg (Chair, AEC), Pief, Wallace Sterling (Stanford University President), Don Hornig (President's Science Advisor), Ed Ginzton (Varian Associates CEO). (Credit: Stanford University News Service.)*

This section is followed by a long chapter describing the subsequent thirty-year physics research and accelerator improvement programs at SLAC. It is omitted here since it has also been
described in this book.

Science Advising and International Science

Pief's familiarity with the Manhattan Project, his involvements at UCRL, his arrival at Stanford, his drafting of the "Screw-
driver Report" on fissile materials detection with Hofstadter, and
his overall eclectic scientific expertise propelled him as early as
1954 into a very long series of activities and panels having to do
with science advising, first at the NSF, later with the Air Force,
culminating with the President's Science Advisory Committee (PSAC) under George Kistiakowski during the Eisenhower

Administration. As a result, in 1959, while he was taking a sabbatical at CERN, he got involved in his first negotiations with the Soviets. These negotiations eventually culminated in 1963 with the adoption of the Limited Test Ban Treaty with the USSR.

Pief stayed on PSAC until 1964. His experience and thoughts on the roles, responsibilities, conflicts of interest and accountability of science advisors are discussed in detail in the book and should be read by anybody who decides to accept such a position in any government agency.

120

PSAC Meeting in Newport News, July 12, 1960. Pief is seen presenting nuclear test ban report to President Eisenhower across the table. Clockwise from left to right: Mannie Piore, Don Hornig, George Kistiakowski, President Eisenhower, George Beadle, unknown, John Tukey, unknown, John Bardeen, Jim Killian, Al Weinberg, W. Panofsky, Jerry Wiesner, Wally Z, Detlev Bronk. (Credit: SLAC Archives and History Office, Panofsky Collection.)

In addition to his service to various U.S. government panels, and to Stanford University in Prof. Franklin's dismissal controversy, Pief also began to play a major role in international scientific organizations such as the International Union of Pure and Applied Physics (IUPAP), and was invited to many conferences to give talks and reports.

In the late 1970's, partially because of his efforts, various government-to-government collaborative science agreements were signed by the US with the Soviets, the Japanese and the People's Republic of China (PRC), and annual cooperative meetings were held on high energy physics. Pief attended many of these and played major roles in the collaborations. With the PRC, he and TD Lee deserve personal credit for having encouraged and helped the Chinese to build the BEPC electron-positron colliding beam facility in Beijing. To get them started in this direction, in the summer of 1982 Pief invited a delegation of about thirty Chinese physicists and engineers to SLAC to produce a preliminary design of the machine. This relationship has survived for over 25 years despite occasional problems, including the 1989 Tiananmen events which Pief personally deplored. Pief with others was responsible during the October 14th, 1998 U.S.-PRC meeting in Beijing for briefing Premier Zhu Rongji to approve the BEPC II upgrade.

Arms Control (1981-2007): the Unfinished Business

The control and drastic reduction of nuclear weapons was a challenge Pief confronted daily -- to the last day of his life. He involved himself in every controversy in this area, and even though he sometimes seemed discouraged, he never gave up. What struck me and sometimes disappointed me when Pief talked to me about some aspect of this subject, was that he never departed from rational arguments and did not allow himself

Pief among "giants", Tom Kirk and Chen Hesheng, at the 25th Anniversary US-PRC collaboration meeting in Beijing, October 2004. (Credit: Fred Harris, University of Hawaii.)

to become a polemicist. In a world that is often irrational, and where an uninformed public can be driven by very superficial political arguments, being totally fair doesn't always produce fast results. But by consistently behaving himself in this manner, Pief always retained the respect of his friends and adversaries.

As early as 1965 Pief was recruited to serve as a member of JASON, an ad hoc group of academics who get together every summer to advise the U.S. government on matters of general and national security interest. In 1981, he joined the Committee on International Security and Arms Control (CISAC) of the National Academy of Sciences, a committee he chaired from 1985 to 1993. CISAC started out by holding bilateral discussions with the Russians, but these were later extended to very productive contacts with China, and then with allies such as France, Italy, Germany and the UK. In Italy these contacts developed into the multinational Amaldi conferences which Pief attended.

What positions did Pief take? Pief fundamentally believed that after 1945 and certainly during the Cold War, nuclear war was no longer a possible strategy for any nation, that nuclear weapons could not serve any military function for any nation, except to deter another nation from attacking it with nuclear weapons. For this, the reader is referred to his article written with his friend Spurgeon Keeney on "MAD vs. NUTS", Mutual Assured Destruction vs. Nuclear Utilization Target Selection.

In summary, Pief supported the Limited Test Ban Treaty (LTBT), the Threshold Test Ban Treaty (TTBT), the Ban on Peaceful Nuclear Explosions (PNE), the Nuclear Nonproliferation Treaty (NPT), the Anti- Ballistic Missile Treaty (ABM), and the Comprehensive Test Ban Treaty (CTBT) which unfortunately was never ratified by the U.S. Congress. When President Reagan proposed his Star Wars project, Pief opposed it on technical grounds, arguing scientifically that it would not really work and that the "offense would always outstrip the defense" because it would be less expensive and more effective. During his CISAC chairmanship, Pief argued eloquently against lumping nuclear, chemical and biological under the single WMD label, and against threatening to use nuclear weapons to deter the use of the other two weapons. He also conducted the study for the management and disposition of excess plutonium which came up with recommendations to fabricate mixed oxide fuel (MOX) combining plutonium and uranium oxides for use in reactors, or to mix the plutonium with highly radioactive fission products which would then be disposed of in a geological repository. Presidents George W. Bush and Vladimir Putin signed the Plutonium Management and Disposition Agreement (PMDA) to dispose of 34 tons of plutonium via the MOX process, but because of mutual disagreements over bureaucratic issues, no disposition has yet taken place, seven years later.

Pief ends his book with a strong admonition to the world.

In 2006 there are still close to 30,000 nuclear weapons on the planet (about 13,000 in 2021). Such a number is far in excess of any security need. The risks of inadvertent launches due to faulty communications, desperate regional conflicts, proliferation and theft, are enormous and could be totally devastating for humanity. As long as the U.S. relies on these weapons or continues to reinvent new missions for them (like bunker busters) or new designs (like the Reliable Replacement Warhead, the RRW), other countries will see these weapons as symbols of national power and will be tempted to acquire them. In this connection, in 2006 Pief had met with the Iranian Ambassador at the UN, and until the last day of his life, he was upset that the United States was not negotiating directly with that country on the nuclear problem.

Pief notes that a declaration of "No First-Use" of nuclear weapons has so far been embraced only by China but by none of the other nuclear weapons states. He believes that if adopted by all of them, it would at least motivate and enable them to strive for drastic reductions, revitalize the entire nuclear weapons arms-control drive, and eventually lead to a worldwide prohibition of possessing nuclear weapons. He writes, "The United States, as the unquestioned leader – measured by non-nuclear armaments and economic strength – should have the strongest possible interest in leading the reining-in of nuclear weapons on an irreversible basis."

The world could not honor this wonderful scientist and human being more than by heeding his advice on dealing with this ominous threat to humanity.

Appendix 2

A few thoughts about classified and weapons work at Stanford and SLAC

A remark on this subject at a recent Faculty meeting prompted me to remind my colleagues of the origins of this controversial topic at Stanford and at SLAC.

After WW2 and the Manhattan Project, it was understandable that many governments wanted to protect their countries from another conflagration and disaster, and that defense work had to be protected and pursued essentially forever. The problem was that this belief also promoted arms races all over the world, making war even more dangerous and probable, and that it did not protect us from questionable involvements like the Vietnam War.

When I came to Stanford in 1954 to get my PhD, a sizable fraction of my building, the Electronics Research Laboratory, was fenced off for classified work. Nobody on the outside knew what kind of research was being conducted there. Other parts of the campus were in the same situation. Nobody questioned this state of affairs.

It wasn't until the late 60's and early 70's that the student rebellion at Stanford against the Vietnam War forced the University to ban all classified work on campus, to move some of the existing classified programs to SRI, and to separate the management of SRI from that of the University. Note that there was no distinction at the time between classified and defense work: they were one and the same. The motive for rejection of classified work at the University was not that universities are there to diffuse knowledge, not to restrict it, but that universities should not be militarized, on principle. At the time, Stanford also abandoned the ROTC program.

In 1983 during the Cold War, Edward Teller promoted his Star Wars Program at LLNL and convinced President Reagan that his nuclear-generated x-ray laser could destroy incoming Soviet ICBMs in outer space. Teller's proposal created a huge controversy. Two or three LLNL scientists came out in the open and claimed that the whole idea was totally flawed. One of them lost his security clearance in the process. However, LLNL management nevertheless came to Stanford and SSRL (not organizationally part of SLAC at the time) to propose testing some instruments necessary for the development of the weapon with the SPEAR synchrotron radiation beams. When Stanford said that no classified work could be done at the University, LLNL changed its tune and said that the instrument tests per se would not be classified.

When our SLAC staff learned of this, a huge uproar arose, and more than 200 members signed a petition saying that they did not want to participate in delivering beams to SSRL for these experiments. I was one of them. The objection was based on "involuntary servitude" forcing us to work on something to which we deeply objected, on moral grounds. But Donald Kennedy, President of the University, and Art Bienenstock, head of SSRL, said that they could not turn the work down since it was not classified. Panofsky, director of SLAC, could not intervene in our favor, even though he sympathized on principle with our position. So SSRL accepted to do the work. We were all very upset.

Several weeks or months later, for some reason unknown to me, LLNL decided not to do the tests at SSRL. Somehow, we lucked out by default.

This entire incident was a serious lesson. It was not the last time that people coming from industry and other labs thought of involving SLAC in military work. The temptation is always there, based on patriotic motives and national security interests.

For the future, it seems to me that the criterion should not just be to reject classified work. One thing is to work on some technology that can benefit all of humankind but may collaterally also help in the development of a new lethal weapon. This is hard to avoid. Another thing is to use SLAC directly to develop such a weapon. This type of work should be left to the know-how and hopefully the wisdom of NNSA labs.

Appendix 3

Touring Oaxaca with a wise taxi driver December 30 & 31, 2004

Unlike the earlier appendices, this one doesn't seem to have anything to do with SLAC, Stanford or politics. And yet, without SLAC, it would probably not have happened.

One of the first people I hired into my group in 1962 was Alan Wilmunder, the electronics engineer who would design the klystron phasing system. Alan was an excellent engineer, but he also had a strange hobby: he bought narrow gauge locomotives from Central America and brought them to California to run them somewhere. This familiarity with Central America, after a while, made him discover a U.S. program called "Amigos de las Americas," This program to train young U.S. adolescents to do volunteer work in rural areas of Latin America was looking for somebody to head a chapter in Palo Alto, and Alan took on this unpaid job, in addition to his SLAC job. When he described the Amigos program to me, I mentioned it to my wife Gilda, and she immediately thought that this was something our kids should volunteer for. And so, it turned out that Neil was the first to volunteer to give immunizations to people in a village in Nicaragua, Florence to build latrines in a village in Central Mexico, and George to build latrines in a small village near Oaxaca, in Southern Mexico. This is how George got to visit Oaxaca and love it. Years later he recommended I go there on a vacation, and at the end of December 2004, following his advice, I spent a week's vacation there. Thank you, Alan!

Oaxaca has become a large city with sprawling outskirts plagued by traffic jams, poverty, and some fairly ugly suburbs. But the center of town is still today a beautiful example of what some Latin American cities must have looked like 150 years ago: lively streets and plazas lined by stylish colonial old buildings, showing us the superposition of a Spanish heritage on an indigenous civilization that in this case is recognized to be 10,000 years old and a cradle of religious thought. Walking around downtown Oaxaca, one can easily imagine how some of the famous natives like Governor Benito Juarez, General Porfirio Diaz, and painter Rufino Tamayo grew up there and roamed around the streets.

Oaxaca around New Year's was fully booked, but after encountering some difficulties in finding a place to stay, I was able to get a room at La Victoria, a beautiful hotel with a spectacular view of the entire city and a marvelous pool, about ten minutes by car from the center of town.

It was in the morning of December 30th, as I ordered a cab to get from La Victoria to the center, that I was picked up by a very simpatico and talkative taxi driver called Hector, the central character in this little story. It did not take very much time before Hector and I were involved in a lively conversation. I asked him about Benito Juarez's house (now a museum) that is in Oaxaca because Juarez, born in a small neighboring village, grew up and studied there, and eventually became governor and president. After a few exchanges, Hector asked me if I knew Juarez had been a Mason. This led to a conversation about Masons and their attitude towards the Church. Hector told me that he thought Juarez, a Zapotec, had also been Catholic. It seems, however, that his Masonic connection must have driven him to become the architect of Mexican secularism: when he was elected president, he nationalized all the Church's land, instituted freedom of religion and secularized all the hospitals in Mexico.

By this time in the conversation, we had reached my destination but since I was planning to visit Monte Alban in the afternoon and Hector seemed like a rather interesting companion, I engaged him to drive me there a little later. On the road to Monte Alban, which is about half-an-hour from Oaxaca, Hector told me that his profession was really Odontology (a form of dentistry) but that in recent years he had reached the conclusion that he could no longer make a living in this profession, and although he had kept his *"consultorio"* (his office), he was doing better as a taxi driver.

Hector was born in Oaxaca around 1951. When he was one year old, his father abandoned his mother with him and his older brother, and he grew up in great poverty. There was no electricity in his house, only kerosene lamps. But Hector was determined to get a good education and so he made it all the way through high school. At this point he decided he wanted to become a doctor and he entered Medical School in Oaxaca. These were the late 60's and students in Mexico, much like in Europe and in the US, were very socially conscious and got involved in all sorts of human rights and anti-governmental movements. Hector joined a group of students inside the University which was trying to dislodge a clique of entrenched professors who were not really teaching, and one fine morning, he and his friends found themselves expelled from Med School. As he was now ostracized and his chances of getting back into the University of Oaxaca were totally blocked, he left for Mexico City. When he tried to enter Med School in the capital, he was told that they would not recognize the first two or three years he had studied in Oaxaca, and he became quite desperate. But luck had it that by sheer coincidence, he ran into an older high school colleague from Oaxaca who was either studying or had a position in the school of Odontology in the District. This friend helped him get admitted to the school from which he eventually graduated, and he was able to start his career.

When Hector returned to Oaxaca to get established, he was very upset to find that some of his colleagues who had stayed behind at the University, had gone through very hard times: the Police and the Military had brutally repressed the student movement and some of the students had been killed or had disappeared. Hector eventually married in Oaxaca and had two or three children. They are all grown now, have moved to Mexico City and work in various computer software jobs. His wife has died of a heart disease and he lives by himself.

Hector, since his university days, continues to be politically progressive but he has reached the conclusion that one cannot change Mexican society by force. In his free time, he tries to be involved in social reform, but he thinks one must work by example. Hector believes that current President Vicente Fox is a decent well-meaning man, but that most politicians below him in the PAN Party are probably corrupt. The PRI has blocked most of the changes Fox has tried to enact. In Oaxaca, the PRI politicians are still in power, and they are all corrupt as well. Of course, I had no way to verify these assertions, but the newspapers seemed to be full of scandals to confirm them. The population, according to Hector, is incredibly gullible and continues to vote for the same parties. Education is poor, and people don't learn to question anything very deeply. Even Sub-Comandante Marcos of the Zapatista Liberation Army in neighboring Chiapas seems to have mellowed and retrenched from his opportunity to create a national movement. Many of the poor men who cannot make a living in the states of Oaxaca and Chiapas come over to the US illegally: they first must scrape up US $1500/ head that they pay the so-called Coyotes who, after leading them through the desert for three nights, get them across the border.

Hector is very interested in the Ecological Movement. He hates the way most zoos and circuses in Mexico treat animals and he teaches young people to boycott circuses. He gets trees from the Municipality for free and tries to encourage his neighbors to plant these trees. He told me they always find excuses for not planting them. His ambition is to buy a plot of land outside of Oaxaca and to build an adobe house which will be environmentally sound, require little energy to heat and be cool in the summer. He has a whole plan to build this house. Meanwhile, he has become a licensed "driver-ed" volunteer, and he spends a fair amount of time teaching Indians to drive. Outside of Oaxaca, there is a huge indigenous population, Zapotecs and many other groups, who barely speak Spanish. Most of these populations still live under the Ley Indigena. Hector thinks this body of laws is discriminatory and hardly makes sense anymore, even if originally it protected the Indians in some ways. He said: "Look at us, the vast majority in this country, we are Mestizos, most of us have Indian blood!"

I spent close to two hours walking around Monte Alban, the most formidable Zapotec archaeological site (500BC-800AD) in the area. According to Hector, it is not clear whether it was a gigantic city, a military fortress, a religious shrine, or all the above at some time. But it is huge, has multiple pyramids, columns, a ball game stadium, tombs, terraces, patios, stelae representing dancers or prisoners about to be sacrificed, and endless stairs reaching up to elevated platforms. Monte Alban is a wonderful complement to the Mayan sites of Yucatan. In this connection, while I was there, I read that one of the reasons (or excuses) Cortez and the other Spanish Conquistadors found for subjugating and Christianizing the Indians was that they wanted to stamp out their practice of human sacrifice: it was something to which they could feel superior while they were plundering them.

Hector waited for me outside of Monte Alban, and we then

drove on south to San Bartolo Coyotepec. This small village is famous for the mud pottery that is made there. The interesting feature of this pottery is that the brown mud that is used as raw material turns pitch black upon firing and it is quite decorative. As one drives around the area, another surprising feature of these outskirts of Oaxaca is that there are police checkpoints along the roads where taxi drivers must stop. Apparently, some drivers have been assaulted in the last few years, and so the police keep track of both the drivers and the passengers when they leave town and return.

Since I had learned so much from Hector that day, I asked him to drive me to other sites the next day, in the afternoon (his taxi was used by another driver in the morning).

Thus, on the 31st, we drove 50 kms east to Mitla. Mitla is another famous archaeological site, much smaller than Monte Alban, which dates back to 1350 AD, after the invasion of the Mixtecs, a later indigenous group. It consists of several square courtyards with interesting columns and highly decorated mosaics and painted stone buildings. Immediately adjacent to the site, there is a Christian church with red steeples that apparently was built with stones recycled from the original Mixtec buildings, and right outside, there is a lively indigenous market. The whole complex is remarkably interesting. Close to Mitla, there is yet another site called Yagul (800 AD) that has another famous ball game and a labyrinth, which I did not get to see. Eventually the whole area was overrun by the Aztecs (also called Mexicas) who founded the city of Huaxyacac (the name for Oaxaca in the Nahuatl language).

On the way back to Oaxaca, Hector took me to the small town of Tlacolula where there is a famous Dominican church and convent. This church is a small version of the magnificent Templo, Museo and Jardin Botanico de Santo Domingo in downtown Oaxaca, around the corner from the Hotel Camino Real. Like Santo Domingo, it is totally baroque. It consists of two perpendicular buildings, a main section, and a chapel. Wherever one looks, there are golden decorations with paintings and sculptured faces of saints and martyrs. What is unique about the sculptures is that they were carved out of the very stones that make up the interior walls of the chapel. There is also an elegant black and white stone fence that was recently found intact in a basement behind the church and installed in front of the altar. Tlacolula is equally famous because of the Mescal (a liqueur) that is made in the area.

While we were driving around, Hector told me that he has a number of friends in that area and that he is frequently invited to weddings. Weddings are the occasion for huge feasts and celebrations. The ceremonies follow all kinds of traditions, some of them quite medieval. Guests are expected to bring important gifts and the hosts keep track for a long time of who brought what. Gifts can range from bottles of wine to pigs or other animals. When at a later date another wedding takes place in the family of a guest, the hosts are supposed to reciprocate with the same gift. Until recently, the weddings could last several days, and the guests stayed in the villages with the couple's families. On the specific wedding night, at some determined time, all music and conversation stop, and the bride and groom disappear in the nuptial room. After some time, the groom is supposed to emerge from the room with a blood-stained sheet, proof that the bride was a virgin. Everybody is there to witness the event. If there is no blood, it is a total disaster, and the wedding is annulled. Not only is the bride's family disgraced but they must return all the gifts and pay for whatever expenses the groom's family incurred. Hector told me that in recent years, this tradition had mellowed and the younger couples (who often have already slept together) tend to cheat, cut their fingers with a knife, and use that blood to stain the sheet! I guess some problems have a solution!

By this time, it was about 6:00 PM and we were driving back to Oaxaca. Hector asked me what I was going to do for New Year's Eve, and I indicated that I wanted to return to La Victoria to have dinner there. At this point he told me that in the last few years since his wife had died, he had decided to do something different on this occasion. Apparently, there are a lot of extremely poor hospitals in Oaxaca and the families of sick people spend the nights sitting around the waiting rooms to keep the sick company. It occurred to Hector that it would be a good idea to educate young people to do something cheerful but constructive that evening. For this purpose, he has mobilized a whole group of youngsters who during the day prepare many "tortas" (these are pies with meat) and starting around 11:00 PM load all these piles of tortas onto a truck and make the rounds to all the hospitals in the city, bringing them to the poor people in the waiting rooms. Apparently, this operation is a great success, and the families are enormously appreciative. As the New Year came and I was watching the city and the fireworks from my hotel terrace, Hector and his crew were involved in this wonderful gesture! The last two days of my stay, Hector did not have his taxi and I unfortunately did not see him again, nor did I communicate with him, but I certainly never forgot him.

The story is a tribute to humankind. In 2021, I dedicated it to the memory of Max Lenail, son of my close friends Ben Lenail and Laurie Yoler of Palo Alto. Max, an unusually talented young man, died at age 21 in a fateful accident while jogging during a sudden hailstorm in a park near San Diego, California.

Appendix 4

Some of my favorites

Some books read in French
Les trois mousquetaires, d'Alexandre Dumas
Autour du monde en quatre-vingt jours, de Jules Verne
L'Iliade et l'Odyssée, de Homère
Madame Bovary, de Gustave Flaubert
Cyrano de Bergerac, d'Edmond Rostand
Le Dr. Jivago, de Boris Pasternak
Les faux-monnayeurs, d'André Gide
La condition humaine, d'André Malraux
L'antisémitisme, de Jean-Paul Sartre
La promesse de l'aube, de Romain Gary

Some books read in English
War and Peace, by Leo Tolstoy
On the Origin of the Species, by Charles Darwin
For Whom the Bell Tolls, by Ernest Hemingway
Curious George, by Margaret and H.A. Rey
Memoirs, by Winston Churchill
People of the Lake, by Richard Leakey and Roger Lewin
The Anatomy of Human Aggression, by Eric Fromm
QED, by Richard Feynman
Why Nations Go to War, by John Stoessinger
The Portrait of a Lady, by Henry James
A Promised Land, by Barack Obama
A Crack in Creation, by Jennifer Doudna

Composers

J.S. Bach, Mozart, Beethoven, Mendelsohn. Brahms, Offenbach, Debussy, Ravel, Prokofiev, Stravinsky

Operas

The Marriage of Figaro, by Mozart
Don Giovanni, by Mozart
The Barber of Seville, by Rossini
Elixir d'amore, by Donizetti
Traviata and Aida, by Verdi
Walkure, Meistersinger, and *Tannhauser*, by Wagner
Eugene Onegin, by Tchaikovsky
Carmen, by Bizet
Tosca, by Puccini
Der Rosenkavalier, by Richard Strauss

Popular singers

Carlos Gardel, Maurice Chevalier, Edith Piaf, Charles Trénet, Elvis Presley, The Beatles

Movies

City Lights, and *Modern Times* (Chaplin)
A nous la liberté (René Clair)
Napoléon (Abel Gance)
Les enfants du paradis (Marcel Carné)
Le diable au corps.
Gone with the wind
Casablanca
Showboat
Scarlet Pimpernel
The Third Man
All Fred Astaire and Ginger Rogers movies
Lawrence of Arabia
Schindler's List
Saving Private Ryan

Cities

Paris, San Francisco, Venice, New York. Rome, Sienna, Florence, London, Seville, Prague, Dubrovnik, Athens, Jerusalem

Painters

Giotto
Piero della Francesca
Giovanni Bellini
Leonardo da Vinci
Michelangelo
Goya
Renoir, Monet, Manet
Gauguin
Picasso
Matisse

And an unknown painter of my great-great uncle R. Loew in Prague (1846), to whom my son George Loew, five generations later, bears some resemblance:

Index

CPSIA information can be obtained
at www.ICGtesting.com
Printed in the USA
JSHW041037160623
42833JS00001BB/1

9 781587 906466